the cure

on record

BY DAREN BUTLER

Edited by Chris Charlesworth
Cover & Book designed by Alun Evans, 4i Limited
Picture research by Daren Butler

ISBN: 0.7119.3867.9
Order No.OP47600

Exclusive Distributors:
Book Sales Limited,
8/9 Frith Street,
London W1V 5TZ, UK.

Music Sales Corporation,
257 Park Avenue South,
New York, NY10010, USA.

Music Sales Pty Limited,
Lisgar House, 30-32 Carrington Street,
Sydney, NSW2000, Australia.

To the Music Trade only:
Music Sales Limited,
8/9 Frith Street,
London W1V 5TZ, UK.

Photo credits:
Tom Sheehan 46, 51, 52, Paul Cox 74,
79, 90, 92, 103, 104, 111, 128, Paul
Slattery 4, 5, 18, Redferns 28, Rex
Features 30, 101, London Features
International 12, 22, 37, 57, 60, 87, 119,
123, 125, Retna 112, 115, Andy Vella 11,
Fiction Records 13, 15, 30, 31.

Every effort has been made to trace the
copyright holders of the photographs in this
book but one or two were unreachable.
We would be grateful if the photographers
concerned would contact us.

Printed & bound in Singapore.

A catalogue record of this book is
available from the British Library.

INTRODUCTION

The longevity and worldwide success of The Cure has brought with it a great variety of singles and albums. Since the release of their first record in 1978 to the present day, Cure singles and albums have appeared in a myriad of differing pressings and sleeves.

Scattered among them are many obscure and unusual releases, with different picture sleeves, different B sides, varied packaging and others that have remained totally unreleased. Inevitably, these have become collectable. They also stand as fascinating examples of how different countries have presented and promoted releases by The Cure.

This book takes a comprehensive look at the discography of The Cure, including the rarest and many of the most unusual official pressings of singles, albums and CDs. Regardless of the rarity, and the varying degree of interest that surrounds these worldwide pressings, none would hold any value at all without the music of THE CURE.

With thanks and appreciation to The Cure and Fiction Records for their kind permission and co-operation in the production of this book.

THREE IMAGINARY BOYS

UK RELEASE DATE – MAY, 1979
LP FIX 1
Cassette FIXC1
CD 827686-2

Line up:
Robert Smith,
Michael Dempsey,
Laurence Tolhurst

Side One
10.15 Saturday Night
Accuracy
Grinding Halt
Another Day
Object
Subway Song

Side Two
Foxy Lady
Meat Hook
So What
Fire In Cairo
It's Not You
Three Imaginary Boys
The Weedy Burton

Original copies of the 'Three Imaginary Boys' LP were first issued with a postcard and a badge of the sleeve design.

A total of four different promotional postcards was issued by Polydor. Three of them made a set which, when joined together, spell "The Cure Three Imaginary Boys". Each one had a different message on the back: "Keep with other one", "Keep this", and "Well done! Now throw them away".

The short untitled instrumental track at the end of side two of 'Three Imaginary Boys' (which is not referred to on the sleeve or label) was recorded under the title "The Weedy Burton". It derived from Michael Dempsey's amusement at the book 'Play in a Day', written by 1950s guitarist Bert Weedon.

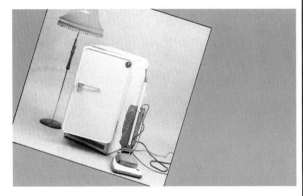

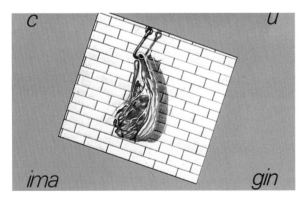

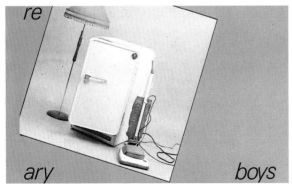

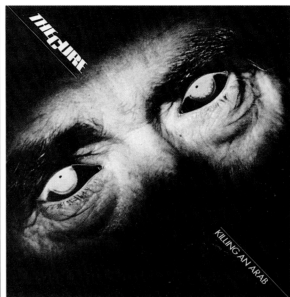

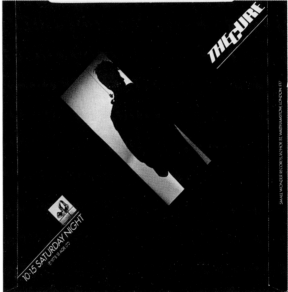

reverse

KILLING AN ARAB b/w 10.15 SATURDAY NIGHT

UK release – December, 1978. After many demos for the first deal with Hansa Records and then with Chris Parry and Fiction Records, 'Killing An Arab' b/w '10.15 Saturday Night' (small 11) was released in December, 1978, as The Cure's first ever single.

Although The Cure were signed to 18 Age/Fiction, the first 15,000 copies were pressed in Ireland and released on Small Wonder Records in an attempted rush release before Christmas. Despite this, it was not actually released until just after Christmas, 1978. No promotional copies were issued.

Two months later in February, 1979, 'Killing An Arab' (FICS 001) was re-issued on Fiction Records, as the label's first ever release, and distributed by Polydor Records. Again, 15,000 copies were pressed. The A and B sides remained the same and the sleeve, designed by Chris Parry and Bill Smith, was only very slightly different on the reverse, (with the Small Wonder issue depicting a small dripping tap). This Fiction issue, also released only in the UK, had injection mould labels and not paper labels.

During the campaign to promote 'Killing An Arab' Polydor distributed the book, *The Outsider* by Albert Camus, with copies of this single as a promotional exercise.

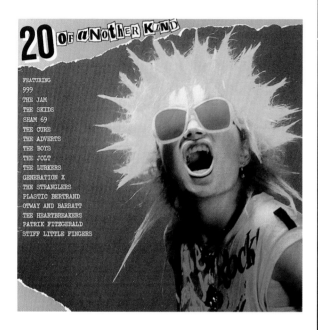

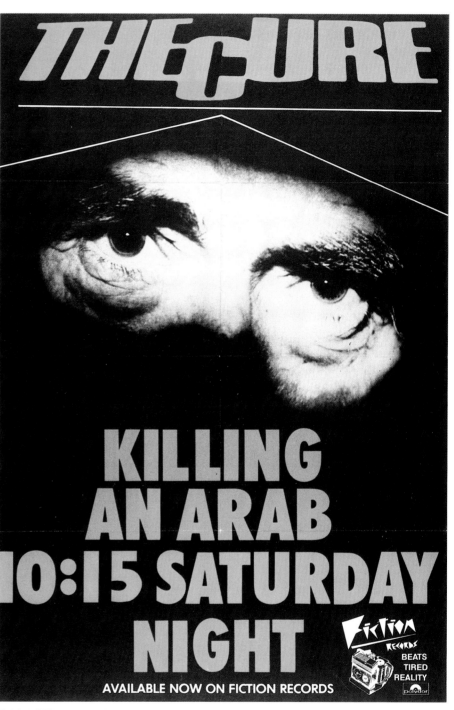

In the same month, 'Killing An Arab' was included on '20 Of Another Kind', a post - punk compilation put together by Chris Parry and released by Polydor Records. The label and sleeve credits 'Killing An Arab' to Dempsey, Smith and a misprinted Polhurst. (LP POLS1006.)

The Cure's original contract with Chris Parry was actually signed with 18 Age Records. Although this name was quickly changed to Fiction, both names, 18 Age Records and Fiction Records, are credited on all releases until 1982 when the name '18 Age Records' was discarded.

Original 1979 promotional poster for 'Killing An Arab'. Note the eyes are not reversed.

GRINDING HALT b/w MEATHOOK

UK 12"(CUR 1)

Issued – May 1979

This unique promotional only 12" of 'Grinding Halt' was specially pressed, more as a promotion for 'Three Imaginary Boys' than as a possible second single.

Approximately 1,500 12" copies were pressed with 'Meathook' as the B side and issued with only a white sleeve with a title sticker, and distributed in the UK around clubs and radio stations at a time when 12" pressings were issued infrequently. This record has remained as a promotional only pressing.

Neither Chris Parry nor Fiction Records commissioned any 7" pressings of 'Grinding Halt' to be pressed.

In 1980 'Grinding Halt' also appeared in the American film *Times Square* and was included on the sound track double LP, released on the RSO label and distributed by Polydor. The sleeve of UK copies (RSO 2658145) was very slightly different from US copies (RS 24203).

BOYS DON'T CRY b/w PLASTIC PASSION

UK 7" (FICS 002)

UK Release – June, 1979.

Subsequent to the promo only 'Grinding Halt' 12", 'Boys Don't Cry' b/w 'Plastic Passion' was released as the second single and was also The Cure's first single released outside the UK (in four other countries). Again, this sleeve was designed by Bill Smith.

A very small number of promotional copies (FICS 002) were also distributed in the UK in standard sleeves, also b/w 'Plastic Passion', but note the NOT FOR SALE label stamp on this issue and the missing letter "A" which is normally found on the A side label of the standard copies.

Irish copies of 'Boys Don't Cry' (FICS 002) were pressed separately in the Republic of Ireland. These have red paper Polydor labels instead of the injection mould type, but were distributed with the same picture sleeve and tracks as the UK copy, but again are much rarer. This was the first Cure single released under an Irish label. Each of these three pressings have the same cryptic inscription in the run off groove. Side A reads "But Bill does", a reference to Chris Parry. Side B reads "From the land of 1,000 microphones", which refers to The Cure's surprise at the number of microphones needed to record the drums on 'Boys Don't Cry'.

Later in the year, 'Boys Don't Cry' was included on a second '20 Of Another Kind' compilation album released by Polydor. Once rumoured to exist, was an American commercial release of 'Boys Don't Cry' b/w 'Jumping Someone Else's Train' on the PVC label, but in fact, this pressing does not exist.

BOYS DON'T CRY b/w PLASTIC PASSION

POLYDOR (28 14 215)
SPANISH PROMOTIONAL
ONLY 7'' PRESSING
Issued – 1980

There is no doubt this is the rarest issue of 'Boys Don't Cry' and is definitely one of the most rare and obscure promotional only records by The Cure.

It was issued in 1980 as one of six different 7'' singles, each by a different UK artist, in a promotional only box set entitled 'On The Wave'. This included the likes of The Acrylics and The Invaders, all in textured black and white sleeves. This box was issued by Polydor exclusively in Spain.

This promotional only 7'' of 'Boys Don't Cry' is also b/w 'Plastic Passion', but merits great interest for its unique promo picture sleeve with a brief biography on the reverse and, of course, its extreme scarcity. Note the words ''Ejemplar Gratuito Prohibida Su Venta'' on the sleeve and label meaning ''Promo only, not for sale''.

Later in 1980, 'On The Wave' was released commercially, but only as a compilation LP (Polydor 2482482) and included the track 'Boys Don't Cry'. In the same year 'Boys Don't Cry' was also released commercially as a single in Spain, again with 'Plastic Passion' as the B side but with the same sleeve as the UK issue. (Polydor 2059 143).

THE CURE:

En la actualidad, son muchos los grupos que van surgiendo, quedándose la mayoría de ellos en sus lugares de origen para llevar una vida de pequeños clubs locales. A lo sumo graban un par de singles en una pequeña compañía que nunca logrará sacarlos del anonimato. Y desaparecen al poco tiempo sin más.

Los afortunados que rompen la barrera y se labran una fama entre un cierto sector de público, lo consiguen mediante un esfuerzo enorme pero que si no va acompañado de una garra y una calidad indiscutible, desaparecen por muchos padrinos que les apoyen.

THE CURE, sin haber conseguido el "hit" que les llevara al "top" de las listas, son el grupo que goza de mejor salud de cara a un futuro inmediato. Las votaciones de los lectores de las revistas especializadas y "del rollo" los sitúan invariablemente detrás de dos grupos de "portada" y por delante de recientes números 1. En tales circunstancias, de cara a 1980, cabe esperar su consagración definitiva.

THE CURE ha funcionado como trio hasta octubre del 79. Más de un año de rodaje en giras, ganando seguidores en cada ciudad, teloneros de artistas "mayores", con el handicap que supone enfrentarse con una sala que no venía a verlos a ellos.

En octubre tiene lugar un reajuste en la banda. MICHAEL DEMPSEY hasta entonces bajo del grupo, es sustituido por SIMO GALLUP (bajo) y MATTHEW HARTLEY (teclados). Se ponen a ensayar para acometer una gira por el Reino Unido a finales de noviembre y principios de diciembre. Más tarde, dan un salto al continente, y actuan en 11 sitios distintos por Francia, Holanda y Bélgica. Pero todo ésto esperando su debut en USA donde su álbum debe publicarse en la primavera del 80.

Sus orígenes son el de una típica familia de clase media inglesa. Musicalmente, fueron en tiempos un quinteto llamado THE EASY CURE.

ROBERT SMITH, líder de la banda, recordaba a propósito de los viejos tiempos: "La razón por la que no teníamos una imagen entonces era que no estabamos afiliados a nada. No había ni ala derecha, ni izquierda, ni había nada".

La música es lo único que les une. ROBERT dice: "el que nos guste tocar las mismas cosas no quiere decir que tengamos que creer en las mismas cosas, y mucho menos gustarnos. En la realidad no tengo porqué llevarme bien con ellos. Realmente no tengo que hacerlo con nadie".

"BOYS DON'T CRY" junto a "10.15" y "ACCURACY" son las canciones favoritas de ROBERT SMITH de la primera época de THE CURE como trio. "Es muy pop, me gusta, pero me alegro de que no haya sido un enorme éxito, sería monstruoso que la gente viniera ahora a exigirnos que hiciéramos siempre hits en ese estilo".

LOL TOLHURST, el cuarto miembro del grupo, comenta a propósito de los sesudos que buscan un significado a cada canción que escuchan: "El que sepa lo que quiere decir "Killing an Arab" que venga y me lo cuente".

THE CURE son realmente algo aparte, nada parecido al resto de los grupos. Y no son precisamente algo "IMAGINARIO".

reverse

Both releases merit interest for their differences from the UK release.

The Australian issue (MS 399) replaces the original UK B side 'Plastic Passion' with '10.15 Saturday Night'. Consequently this sleeve does not have the Plastic Passion doll on the reverse, but has the same design on each side of the sleeve.

BOYS DON'T CRY b/w JUMPING SOMEONE ELSE'S TRAIN and KILLING AN ARAB
NEW ZEALAND 7''
STUNN (BFA 001)

The New Zealand pressing of 'Boys Don't Cry' is a distinctive and particularly rare issue among the early Cure singles. It is the only three–track EP 7'' that has been released by The Cure. It featured the first 3 singles, 'Boys Don't Cry' b/w 'Killing an Arab' and 'Jumping Someone Else's Train' so as to give exposure to tracks not otherwise released in New Zealand.

Note the difference in the colour blue of the 2 Stunn labels, quickly distinguishing rarer New Zealand pressings from Australian presssings. Again the sleeve has the same black and white design on each side.

BOYS DON'T CRY b/w 10.15 SATURDAY NIGHT
AUSTRALIAN 7'',
STUNN (MS 399)

This was The Cure's first single in Australia and New Zealand and the first on Stunn Records. The Stunn label was based in New Zealand and was run by Terry Condon who was a school friend of Chris Parry from New Zealand. Australian issues on Stunn were distributed by 7 Records, whilst New Zealand issues on Stunn were distributed by CBS. Records.

THE OBTAINERS
YEH, YEH, YEH AND PUSSY WUSSY b/w
THE MAGSPYS
LIFEBLOOD AND BOMBS.
7'' (GLITCH – 1 – A1)
1979

This recording was the first record to be released on 'Dance Fools Dance', a small label started by Robert Smith and Ric Gallup. They pressed only 100 copies of this record which they sold to friends for 50p each. It has two songs by The Obtainers and two by The Magspys, a shortened name from The Magazine Spies.

The Obtainers were Robin Banks on drums and guitar, and Nick Loot on vocals. At the time of recording they were only 11 and 12 years of age. They recorded two songs with Robert Smith at Morgan Studios, 'Yeh, Yeh, Yeh' and 'Pussy Wussy'. This was the same night that the 'Cult Hero' recordings were made and the unreleased 'See The Children' was recorded.

Photo: Andy Vella

JUMPING SOMEONE ELSE'S TRAIN b/w I'M COLD

UK 7" (FICS 005)
UK release – November, 1979
'Jumping Someone Else's Train' was the last recording with Michael Dempsey before his departure from The Cure. It was recorded specifically as a single between albums, but was a less widespread release than 'Boys Don't Cry', being issued in the UK, Ireland, and as the first single by The Cure in Italy. It later appeared on the 'Boys Don't Cry' compilation and 'Standing On A Beach'. The B side track features 'Siouxsie' on backing vocals.

Irish (FICS 005) and Italian (2059 189) pressings both have the same A and B sides as the UK.

The UK and Irish pressings (FICS 005) have the inscription "Two into three is less than one" in the A side run off groove but have no inscription on the B side. The Irish pressing was issued without a picture sleeve and with a red Polydor sleeve and label.

The sleeve of the scarce Italian pressing differs slightly from the UK release by having a white border around the design on the reverse side of the sleeve, which again was a Bill Smith design.

The other side had 'Lifeblood' and 'Bombs' by The Magspys with whom Simon Gallup was playing bass before joining The Cure. 'Lifeblood' featured Carol Thompson (Simon Gallup's girlfriend) on backing vocals. The record was packaged with an insert, and information sheet on the two bands with a track listing and contacts for extra copies. In the run off groove of the A side, the message reads "Boiling Over". Some copies were packaged with slightly different stickers. Three years later in 1982 a second single was released on this label by Animation, another band from Crawley. The Dance Fools Dance label no longer exists.

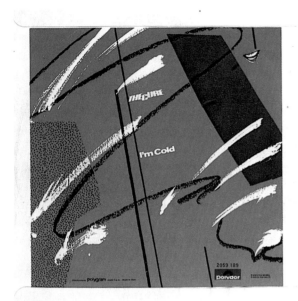

reverse

One month after this release, 'Jumping Someone Else's Train' was included on an eight track, 12'' singles sampler (PROMO 1), issued in the UK by Polydor in December for promotional distribution only. Each artist was introduced by the voice of Alan Black giving brief information on the band, with clapping and applause.

EGTON

WHEN
APPLY TO
BROADCAS

13

CULT HERO
I'M A CULT HERO B/W
I DIG YOU
UK 7" (FICS 006)
UK Release – December, 1979
This recording under the title of
'Cult Hero', was the first by The
Cure together with Simon Gallup
and Porl Thompson amongst an
extended line up of family and
friends, including The Obtainers
and Robert Smith's two sisters,
Janet on bass and Margaret on
backing vocals.

The two songs recorded were
written for, and sung by, 'Frank
Bell', 'The Cult Hero!' who at the
time was the local postman in the
town of Horley.

2,000 copies were pressed in
the UK.. The design for the sleeve
was an idea of Robert Smith's
from an old Howlin' Wolf LP.

reverse

I DIG YOU B/W
I'M A CULT HERO
CANADIAN 7"
MODULATION (MN-45000)
Several months later in 1980 this
single was released in Canada, but
this time with 'I Dig You' as the A
side b/w 'I'm A Cult Hero'.

Its release was prompted by
the popularity in clubs of an
unofficial 12" record that featured
a seven minute version of
'I Dig You', together with songs
by different artists re-mixed into
one track, which was distributed
and played throughout clubs in
Canada. This led to 'I Dig You'
being released on a small third
party deal with Modulation
Records after Polydor Canada
had turned down the chance to
release it. This single was not
issued with a picture sleeve and
sold approximately 35,000 copies.

I DIG YOU B/W
I'M A CULT HERO
NEW ZEALAND 7"
STUNN (BFA 012)
The New Zealand issue of this
single was released in 1981 with
'I Dig You' as the A side b/w 'I'm
A Cult Hero'. It is by far the
rarest of all the releases by 'Cult
Hero' and is one of the most
scarce and rarely found singles by
The Cure. It was issued in a thick
card picture sleeve.

reverse

BRITANNIA WAIVES THE RULES – 12"

AUSTRALIAN (MIST 101)
NEW ZEALAND (BFA 017)
'I Dig You' was not released as a single in Australia, but its B side 'I'm A Cult Hero' did appear in 1981 on 'Britannia Waives The Rules', a very scarce 12'' five track compilation of four bands – Cult Hero, Purple Hearts, The Passions and The Associates who at the time were all on Fiction. Each was produced by Chris Parry.

This is the only record where 'I'm A Cult Hero' appears on a 12''. It was released only in Australia and New Zealand as part of the EMI–Stunn 'Cunning Stunt' series of budget priced record releases.

Note the section of a poster for 'Primary' in the bottom right hand corner of the sleeve.

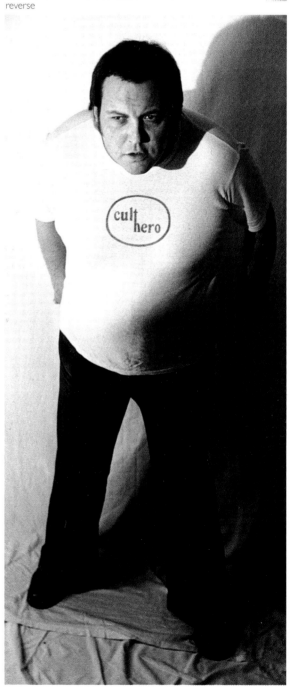

10.15 SATURDAY NIGHT
b/w FOXY LADY
POLYDOR (2814 150)
FRENCH PROMOTIONAL
ONLY 7" PRESSING.

Although never released, this was
the very first record by The Cure
ever pressed in France, featuring a
unique coupling of '10.15 Saturday
Night' b/w 'Foxy Lady' which was
sung by Michael Dempsey.

It was pressed in 1979 purely
as a promotional only record and
other than the 'Three Imaginary
Boys' LP, The Cure's version of
'Foxy Lady' can only be found
on this pressing. This unique
French record was distributed in
a promotional Polydor sleeve and
is probably the very rarest of all
promotional only Cure records.

10.15 SATURDAY NIGHT
b/w ACCURACY
POLYDOR (2059 230)
A year later in 1980, a second
unique pressing of '10.15
Saturday Night' was released as
The Cure's first single in France.
This time with 'Accuracy' as the
B side, another track otherwise
only on 'Three Imaginary Boys'
and the 'Boys Don't Cry' LP.
Besides the album, this record
is the only other commercial
release with this sleeve design.
(Some copies have a corner cut
off and shortly after its release
were sold cheaply in bargain
bins.) As a French only release, it
is considerably rare and, needless
to say, a distinctive pressing
amongst the early singles.

BOYS DON'T CRY
US Release – February 1980

Side One
Jumping Someone Else's Train
Boys Don't Cry
Plastic Passion
10.15 Saturday Night
Accuracy
Object
Subway Song

Side Two
Killing An Arab
Fire In Cairo
Another Day
Grinding Halt
World War
Three Imaginary Boys

The 'Boys Don't Cry' album was originally released in the USA and Canada. It was a compilation of the A sides from the first three UK singles, eight tracks from 'Three Imaginary Boys', 'Plastic Passion' and a new song 'World War' which was recorded during the sessions for 'Three Imaginary Boys' and subsequently rejected. None of these tracks was previously released in the US or Canada.

The US issue was released on PVC Records (PVC 7916) and issued with two different labels. North American Records released it in Canada (NA 024). During 1980 it was also released on the Stunn label in Australia (MLF 353) and New Zealand (Stunn 010).

'Boys Don't Cry' was available in the UK as an import until September 1983 when Fiction released it in the UK on LP (SPELP 26) and cassette (SPEMC 26). The sequence of tracks on both was slightly different from the US version, with 'Boys Don't Cry' opening side one instead of 'Jumping Someone Else's Train'. It was also released in Germany, France and Holland during 1980.

In September, 1986, 'Boys Don't Cry' was released on CD (815011-2). Very early European copies exist with the same 13 tracks as the LP, but later pressings have only 12 tracks. Robert Smith was not happy with 'Object' and disliked 'World War', neither appear on later CD pressings but the track 'So What' was added.

SEVENTEEN SECONDS
UK RELEASE – APRIL, 1980
LP FIX 004
Cassette FIXC 004
CD 825354–2

Line up:
Robert Smith,
Matthieu Hartley,
Laurence Tolhurst,
Simon Gallup

Side One
A Reflection
Play For Today
Secrets
In Your House
Three

Side Two
The Final Sound
A Forest
M
At Night
Seventeen Seconds

A FOREST

UK Release – April, 1980
'A Forest' was commercially more successful in the UK and released in more countries than the previous four singles. On the same day that the video for 'A Forest' was made, one for 'Play For Today' was also filmed. This track was a possible second single to this release and was included on the 1980 Polydor December single sampler 12''. 'A Forest' together with 'Jumping Someone Else's Train' were also included on 'Watch The Wave', a Swedish Polydor compilation album (2982 481).

The UK 7'' (FICS 10) 'A Forest' b/w 'Another Journey By Train' was pressed with both blue and silver injection mould labels. Most copies were issued with picture sleeves while others were issued with Fiction Radiophonic Sleeves. This 3.56 single version is shortened from the version on 'Seventeen Seconds'. The A and B sides remain the same on all 7'' releases.

Rare Irish pressings (FICS 10) have red Polydor labels and sleeve. It was also released on 7'' only in France, Holland and Italy, each with the same catalogue number (Polydor 2059 229) and the same picture sleeve as the UK.

A FOREST b/w ANOTHER JOURNEY BY TRAIN

CANADIAN 7''
POLYDOR (PDS 2098)
This rare Canadian 7'' pressing of 'A Forest' was the only single by The Cure released in Canada on the Polydor label, and other than the 'Cult Hero' 7'' was the first single released there. Note the drill hole through the edge of the label, this was done to records that were being sold off cheaply in the bargain section. It has a picture sleeve the same as the UK.

Original one sided 7'' acetate cut for the single at Strawberry Studios.

A FOREST b/w ANOTHER JOURNEY BY TRAIN.
AUSTRALIAN 7" (MS 416)
NEW ZEALAND 7" (BFA 004)
Only Australian and the rarer New Zealand 7" pressings had this completely different sleeve. It was changed by Stunn without the knowledge or approval of Fiction Records or The Cure. Both sleeves have the same design on each side with only very small differences between them. Both pressings have the same tracks as the UK pressings.

reverse

A FOREST b/w ANOTHER JOURNEY BY TRAIN
UK 12" (FICSX 10)
'A Forest' was the first single by The Cure released on two formats. This additional 12" pressing was the first commercially released 12" by The Cure. It featured the longer 5.50 LP version of 'A Forest' and remained with 'Another Journey By Train' on the B side, and was issued in only a handful of countries. The sleeve was a positive of the 7" sleeve design.

A FOREST b/w ANOTHER JOURNEY BY TRAIN

GERMAN 12''
METRONOME (0930.022)
'A Forest' was the first single in Germany, released on Metronome Music. Both 7'' and 12'' pressings had the same tracks as the UK pressings. The 7'' (Metronome 0030.281) was issued with a picture sleeve the same as the UK, but the 12'' (0930.022) was released with this unique sleeve. It was changed by Metronome and the design is completely identical on each side.

A FOREST

AUSTRALIAN 12"
Four pressings exist of the Australian 12'' of 'A Forest'. None was issued with a picture sleeve. Two of these pressings were issued on green vinyl, one has 'A Forest' 5.53 version b/w 'Another Journey By Train' (MSD 421), and on the other issue the A side begins with 'The Final Sound' as an extra track before 'A Forest' 6.34 b/w 'Another Journey By Train' (ESP – 103).

This extra track is not indicated on the label titles. The only way to distinguish between these two pressings is the time difference on the label and the small label sticker on the second pressing, giving it a different catalogue number (ESP – 103). The majority of this 12'' pressing were on green vinyl, although the latter issue is considerably rarer than the first.

But much rarer than either of these, are the black vinyl copies of each 12'' pressing that exist. Although all four versions of this 12'' were pressed in Australia, it is unclear whether the pressing with ''The Final Sound' was issued with a new and completely different catalogue number, to distinguish it from (MSD 421) or because it may have been used for sale in New Zealand.

'M'

7" ACETATE
Very rarely is there cause for a Cure acetate to be cut outside the UK or away from a recording project (or for it to be used as a promo). So this one sided 7'' acetate of the track 'M' is unusual for this reason. It was one of a number of different tracks by The Cure that Elektra Records had specially cut as individual acetates around 1988/89. It is thought they were cut, for specific promotional use by a handful of American radio stations. Approximately 15–20 acetates of each track were cut which included a number of tracks only ever released on album, including 'The Holy Hour' and 'The Funeral Party'.

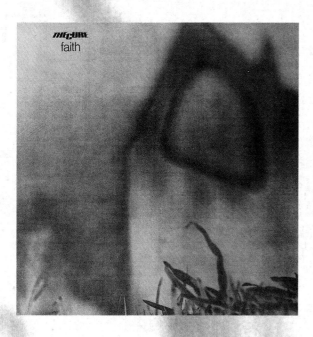

FAITH

UK RELEASE — APRIL, 1981
LP FIX 6
Cassette FIXC 6
CD 827687–2

Line up:
Robert Smith,
Simon Gallup,
Laurence Tolhurst

<u>Side One</u>
The Holy Hour
Primary
Other Voices
All Cats Are Grey

<u>Side Two</u>
The Funeral Party
Doubt
The Drowning Man
Faith

FAITH

This was the first sleeve designed by Parched Art.

The LP 'Faith' was released with a gatefold sleeve in only two countries, Australia and Norway. The Norwegian issue (FIX 6) had the same catalogue number and disc as the UK issue.

The rarer and more interesting Australian release of Faith (MLF 443) was issued not on Stunn, but on 7 Records (on licence from Stunn). Despite this change, the New Zealand issue (Stunn 012) remained on Stunn and was only available with a single sleeve.

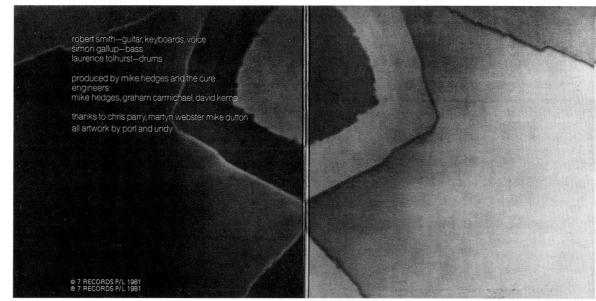

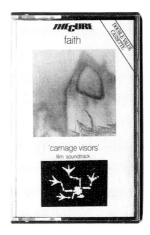

FAITH/CARNAGE VISORS
CASSETTE (FIXC 6)
'Faith' was issued as a double play cassette which on the B side featured the soundtrack to 'Carnage Visors', an animated film which was shown on the 'Picture Tour' in place of a support act and made specially by Simon Gallup's brother, Ric.

Original copies (FIXC 6) were issued with the black and white cover design. Later copies (FIXC 006) were re-issued with a two for the price of one cover design. 'Carnage Visors' is only available on the cassette of 'Faith'. Fiction never pressed any vinyl or test pressings.

PRIMARY

UK Release – May, 1981

As well as the release of 'Primary', the track 'Other Voices' was also considered as a single from 'Faith' and a video for it was made the same day as for 'Primary'. Nevertheless, it has remained unreleased as a single.

The sleeve for 'Primary' was the first design by Parched Art for a single. It did not vary at all amongst foreign releases, other than the Dutch and Australian 7" pressings that included the catalogue number on the front. The A and B sides remained the same as the UK pressings on all releases unless noted.

UK 7" (FICS 12) 'Primary' b/w 'Descent'.

UK 12" (FICSX 12) 'Primary' (5.50 extended version) b/w 'Descent'.

A one sided promo 7" (FICS 12) playing only 'Primary', was issued in the UK, although it does not state promo on the label. On the B side the label is completely blank and it was distributed with a plain white sleeve. It was only released as a 7" in Germany on Metronome (0030.376). German 7" pressings were issued with textured sleeves as standard. Dutch and Spanish copies of the 7" (2059 293) also had a textured sleeve. Worth noting is the Belgian 7" pressing (Polydor 2059 293) as it is thought to be the only Cure single actually pressed in this country.

PRIMARY b/w DESCENT

FRENCH PROMOTIONAL 7"
POLYDOR (2814 262)
'Primary' was never actually released commercially in France on 7" or 12". It exists only as a very scarce unreleased promotional pressing but does not state this on the label. It was issued with a French Polydor promo sleeve. A one sided promotional 7" was also pressed in France, but this is also rarely found.

UK Promo

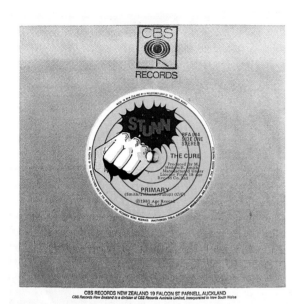

PRIMARY b/w DESCENT
AUSTRALIA AND
NEW ZEALAND
Like 'Faith' the Australian 7'' (MS
480) and 12'' (MSD 493) of
'Primary', both with picture
sleeves, were released on
7 Records and the rarer New
Zealand pressings were released
on Stunn. Some copies of the
New Zealand 7'' (BFA 014) were
issued with CBS sleeves and not
picture sleeves. As well as the
Australian 12'' (MSD 493) on
7 Records, an Australian 12'' of
'Primary' also exists on the Stunn
Label (ESP 104) without a picture
sleeve. It is very likely that it was
actually this pressing that went on
sale in New Zealand despite
being pressed in Australia.

CHARLOTTE SOMETIMES

UK Release – October, 1981

The sleeve design for 'Charlotte Sometimes' was actually a blurred photograph of Mary Poole in an old castle, in Scotland, taken by Robert Smith in 1980. This single was released between 'Faith' and 'Pornography' and did not appear on any LP until 1984 on 'Concert', 'Standing On A Beach' in 1986 and 'Paris' in 1993.

The book *Charlotte Sometimes*, written by Penelope Farmer, mentions The Cure on its cover, acknowledging the book's own influence on the single, and the line ''Splintered In Her Head'' can be found within the book.

A shorter version of 'Charlotte Sometimes' which is missing the last verse can be found on 'Modern Dance', (NE11 56) a K – TEL compilation album.

In 1986 'Charlotte Sometimes' was reissued in Germany and France on 7'' and 12''.

The A and B sides remain the same as the UK issues on all releases.

UK 7'' (FICS 14) 'Charlotte Sometimes' b/w 'Splintered in Her Head'.

UK 12'' (FICSX 14) 'Charlotte Sometimes' and 'Splintered In Her Head' b/w 'Faith' recorded live at Capital Theatre, Sydney, Australia on August 17, 1981.

CHARLOTTE SOMETIMES b/w SPLINTERED IN HER HEAD

SPANISH 7'' (2059 410)

The Spanish pressing of the 7'', typically has a textured sleeve but unlike other issues of the single has the same design on the reverse as the front. Note the larger titles and the Spanish trans-lation (*CHARLOTTE A VECES*). 'Charlotte Sometimes' was also released on 7'' in France, Germany, Holland and Italy with the same catalogue number.

reverse

Original one sided 7'' acetate

French

CHARLOTTE SOMETIMES b/w SPLINTERED IN HER HEAD

NEW ZEALAND 7'' 1982 STUNN (BFA 020).
'Charlotte Sometimes' was not released until 1982 in Australia or New Zealand. The Australian issue (CURE 7001) was released on CBS Records while the New Zealand issue remained on Stunn.

Note the peculiarity on this sleeve of the New Zealand 7''. On both the back and the front it is a complete reverse image of the normal design. Only the New Zealand 7'' is like this.

CHARLOTTE SOMETIMES AND SPLINTERED IN HER HEAD b/w FAITH (LIVE).

AUSTRALIAN 12''
(Cure 12001)
NEW ZEALAND 12''
(STUNN 020)
1982
The very rare New Zealand 12'' of 'Charlotte Sometimes' (STUNN 020) and the more common Australian 12'' (CURE 12001) were the only pressings that give credits on the front of the sleeve for the live recording of 'Faith' to Keith Walker for Mixing, 2JJJ FM for recording and state the venue and date it was recorded.

**CHARLOTTE SOMETIMES
SLINTERED IN HER HEAD
b/w FAITH (LIVE)**
GERMAN 12''
METRONOME (0930.041)
Along with the New Zealand 7''
and 12'', this original 12'' German
pressing is probably the most
scarce of all the releases of
'Charlotte Sometimes'. It is the
only other sleeve with a completely
reversed design on each side, and
like the German 12'' of 'A Forest'
is unique for the additional super
sound single graphics. The
German 7'' pressing was issued
with a standard sleeve same as UK.

reverse

HAPPILY EVER AFTER

A & M RECORDS (SP 6020)
USA RELEASE – SEPTEMBER, 1981.

'Happily Ever After' was released in the US only, as a double album package of 'Seventeen Seconds' and 'Faith' instead of their being released separately. 'Happily Ever After' was sold at a budget price and was also released as a double play cassette (CS 6020). The sleeve was designed by Ben Kelly, who later also worked on the sleeve of 'Pornography'. Later pressings of 'Happily Ever After' can be recognised by pencil shaded labels, and in 1987 A & M released 'Happily Ever After' on a single long play CD (CD 6020).

Neither 'Seventeen Seconds' nor 'Faith' was available in the US as separate LPs until 1986, when they were issued on LP, CD and cassette by Elektra Records.

In Canada both LPs were released separately with 'Seventeen Seconds' (PDS-1-6282) being released on Polydor Records (The Cure's only LP in Canada on this label) and 'Faith' on the A & M label (SP 79801) as was the release of 'Pornography' in both Canada and the US.

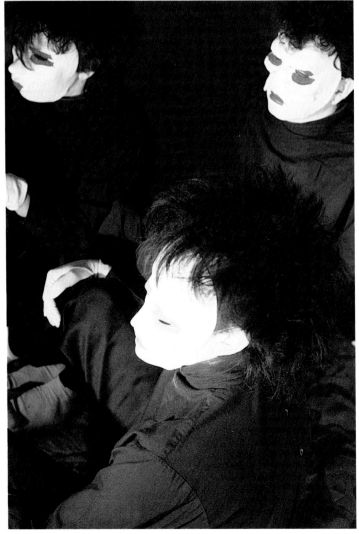

PORNOGRAPHY

UK RELEASE – MAY, 1982
LP FIXD 7
Cassette FIXDC 7
CD 827688–2

Line up:
Robert Smith,
Simon Gallup,
Laurence Tolhurst

Side One
One Hundred Years
A Short Term Effect
The Hanging Garden
Siamese Twins

Side Two
The Figurehead
A Strange Day
Cold
Pornography

PORNOGRAPHY

JAPANESE
VAP (35002–25)
Released 1983

'Pornography' was the first of
The Cure's LPs to be released
in Japan, closely followed by
'Seventeen Seconds' (35101–25)
and 'Faith' (35109–25). They
were all issued in 1983 on VAP, a
small Japanese independent label.

This particular pressing of
'Pornography' includes a gatefold
Japanese lyric sheet with three
photographs of The Cure from
the video for 'The Hanging
Garden' on the front. It is standard
practice for Japanese pressings to
include lyric sheets, a biography
and a discography. In Japan the
paper sash around the sleeve is
called an *obi*, meaning belt.

Although the sleeve of
'Pornography' was designed by
Ben Kelly with The Cure, Porl
Thompson also created a sleeve
for the album which depicted
naked animals falling from the sky,
covering up parts of their bodies
with their arms and paws. It was
not finished in time to be used as
the sleeve.

A massive version of this design
was painted by Porl Thompson
in luminous paint and used as
a back drop during the
Pornography tour.

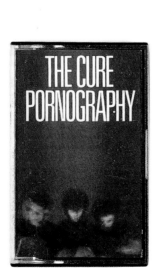

PORNOGRAPHY

CASSETTE (FIXDC 7)
All issues of this cassette were
issued with this sleeve, different
from the LP.

This promotional folder for the 'Pornography' LP was used as an in-house awareness device for Polydor UK sales reps etc. It outlined the marketing campaign and tour dates for the LP and the Fourteen Explicit Moments tour, and housed a copy of the 'One Hundred Years' promo 12''.

Note the difference in the titles on the front of this folder from those on the sleeve of the 'One Hundred Years' promo. Very few of these folders were ever made and items like this are often discarded or thrown away by record company staff. Consequently it is very rare.

THE CURE
PORNOGRAPHY

ALBUM PRODUCED BY THE CURE
ALBUM CAT. NO. FIX 7
MUSICASSETTE CAT. NO. FIXC 7

THE CURE IS

Robert Smith—vocal, guitar, keyboards

Lawrence Tolhurst—drums, keyboards (on album)

Simon Gallup—bass, keyboards (on album)

MARKETING

Extensive campaign to include full page consumer music press advertising. Major instore and window display campaign, flyposting campaign in major cities. Full radio and press and TV coverage.

ON TOUR

19th April	–Reading Hexagon
20th April	–Bristol Colston Hall
21st April	–Brighton Dome
22nd April	–Southampton Gaumont
24th April	–Newcastle City Hall
25th April	–Edinburgh Playhouse
26th April	–Glasgow Pavilion
27th April	–Manchester Apollo
28th April	–Birmingham Odeon
29th April	–Guildford Civic Centre
1st May	–Hammersmith Odeon

PREVIOUS ALBUMS

'Faith' FIX 006

'Three Imaginary Boys' FIX 001

'Seventeen Seconds' FIX 004

RECENT REVIEWS

The Times, Hammersmith Odeon.

Richard Williams.

Melody Maker, of St. George's Hall, Bradford.

Future Cure

FRANK WORRALL

THE CURE
ONE HUNDRED YEARS
THE HANGING GARDEN
FROM THE ALBUM PORNOGRAPHY

ONE HUNDRED YEARS b/w THE HANGING GARDEN (CURE 1)

This rare UK 12'' was pressed specially as a promotional album sampler for 'Pornography'. It featured two tracks from the LP, and was distributed before the release of 'Pornography' with its own unique picture sleeve. A possible French pressing with a thicker sleeve and poster is also rumoured to exist.

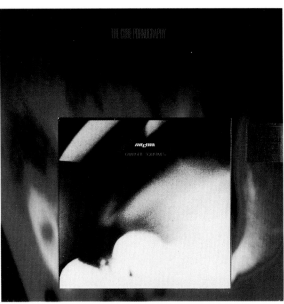

PORNOGRAPHY WITH BONUS CHARLOTTE SOMETIMES 7"

The 'Pornography' LP was originally released in Australia and New Zealand on the Stunn label. However, shortly after the LP's release, the Australian issue (STUN–511) changed to CBS Records (the same label as the Australian issue of 'Charlotte Sometimes').

Shortly after the change to CBS, this special edition of 'Pornography' (CURE 002) was issued with a bonus 7" copy of 'Charlotte Sometimes' (CURE 7001) inside. The package was sealed by the silver sticker on the edge of the sleeve. Each record and sleeve was stamped 'Promotional only'.

Australian and New Zealand pressings of 'Pornography' had red coloured inner sleeves, unlike most other issues which were coloured blue. The New Zealand issue remained on Stunn until the label's demise at the end of 1982 when The Cure changed to Sire Records.

The Cure were also one of the bands included in issue 8 of the Australian magazine/cassette publication *Fast Forward*. This was a 32-page booklet with a double cassette in a black 7" plastic wallet.

Tracks 8 and 9 on the cassette feature an interview with Robert Smith from August, 1981, in Melbourne, Australia, and a live version of 'One Hundred Years' recorded in December, 1981, at Pipbrook Mill, Dorking, Surrey. The booklet included the lyrics to 'One Hundred Years'.

THE HANGING GARDEN b/w KILLING AN ARAB (LIVE)

UK Release – July, 1982
'The Hanging Garden' was released as a single in only four countries. It was released under the title of 'A Single' in the UK and Germany. 'The Hanging Garden' was released one month after the 'Fourteen Explicit Moments Tour', at a time when Simon Gallup had left the band and The Cure had informally dissolved. No 12" pressings were released, but in the UK two 7" editions were released instead.

UK 7" (FICS 15) was b/w a live version of 'Killing An Arab', recorded a few months earlier at the Manchester Apollo on April 27, 1982. Most early copies had paper labels with a new Fiction logo, but less common were copies pressed with injection mould labels.

A scarce Irish pressing was released with the same A and B side tracks, but was issued with red Polydor labels and a Polydor sleeve.

THE CURE 'A SINGLE
THE HANGING GARDEN
KILLING AN ARAB

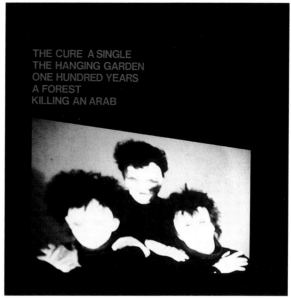

THE CURE A SINGLE
THE HANGING GARDEN
ONE HUNDRED YEARS
A FOREST
KILLING AN ARAB

This double pack of two singles with a gatefold sleeve (FICG 15) was issued and was the first limited edition release by The Cure. Record one included another track from 'Pornography': 'The Hanging Garden' b/w 'One Hundred Years'. Record two included another live track recorded on the 27 April: 'A Forest (Live)' b/w 'Killing An Arab (Live)'. 'The Hanging Garden' was also included on a compilation album 'Modern Heroes' (TVC 1) released by TV Records.

THE CURE
THE HANGING GARDEN 首吊りの庭

15002-07
vap
STEREO
¥700

A STRANGE DAY 奇妙な日

**THE HANGING GARDEN,
ONE HUNDRED YEARS
b/w A FOREST (LIVE),
KILLING AN ARAB (LIVE)**
GERMAN 10"
METRONOME (0930.083)
A 7" single of 'The Hanging
Garden' was not released in
Germany. Instead this 10" press-
ing was released with all four
tracks that were available on the
UK double pack of 'The Hanging
Garden'. This pressing was
unique to Germany, but was
available in the UK on import for
a short period. A small mistake
on the B side label states 'A
Forest' and 'Killing An Arab' were
from the album 'Pornography'.

**THE HANGING GARDEN
b/w A STRANGE DAY**
JAPANESE 7"
VAP (15002-07)
The Cure's first single in Japan
was 'The Hanging Garden'
released in 1983 on the VAP
(Video Audio Project) label. The
only similarity between this
pressing and the UK pressing is
the A side itself.

The unusual sleeve design of
three stills from the video was
put together by VAP and is
consequently unique to the
scarce Japanese pressing. These
three pictures are also on the
front of the lyric booklet that was
included with the rare Japanese
pressing of 'Pornography'.

Another peculiarity of this
pressing is that 'A Strange Day'
replaces the live UK B side 'Killing
An Arab'. 'A Strange Day' does
not appear on any other single
or record other than the
'Pornography' LP itself. White
label promotional copies were
also issued in Japan but were
distributed in very small numbers.

Unlike the pocket style sleeve
from most other countries, the
picture sleeve to this and all
Japanese Cure 7" records are
delicate two sided inserts with
lyrics on the reverse, and the
record in a VAP inner sleeve, all
cotained in a clear bag.

THE CURE A SINGLE
THE HANGING GARDEN
ONE HUNDRED YEARS
A FOREST
KILLING AN ARAB

**THE SINGLES
A FOREST, PRIMARY b/w
CHARLOTTE
SOMETIMES,
THE HANGING GARDEN**
STUNN (CURE 202)
The 'Singles' 12'' was only
released in Australia and was
the last release by The Cure on
Stunn before the label's demise
in late 1982.

It includes 'The Hanging Garden'
which was otherwise not released
in Australia or New Zealand as
a single and also 7'' versions of
'Charlotte Sometimes', 'Primary'
and the 5.50 LP version of 'A
Forest', although it states 5.30
on the label. Together with the
unique sleeve, this is a particularly
distinctive and scarce pressing.

reverse

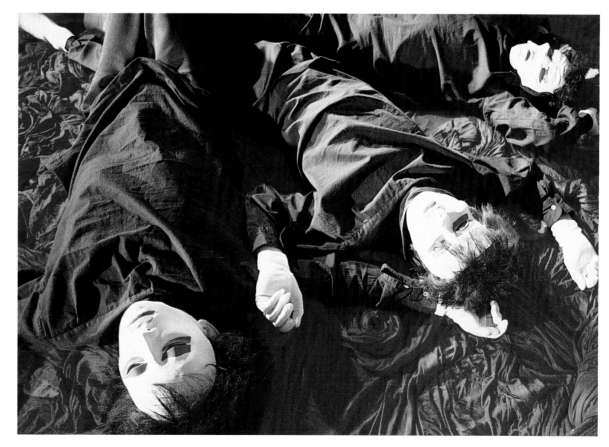

LAMENT FLEXI-DISC

(LYN 12011)

Released 1982

This early version of 'Lament' was recorded exclusively for *Flexi-Pop* magazine and was given away with issue number 22, which, incidentally, did not include a feature on The Cure.

This flexi-disc version is very different from the version later found on 'The Walk' 12'' and 'Japanese Whispers'. It was recorded by Robert Smith and Steve Severin as a one-off at Garden Studios in London.

The majority of these flexi-discs were green, but red copies were also issued, and consequently are considerably more scarce. Some of each colour were also pressed without any titles at all on the disc.

Lyntone, who produced the flexis, also pressed this black one-sided hard vinyl test pressing, which is by far superior in sound quality to the flexi-disc. Lyntone produced no more than approximately 10 copies of this test pressing.

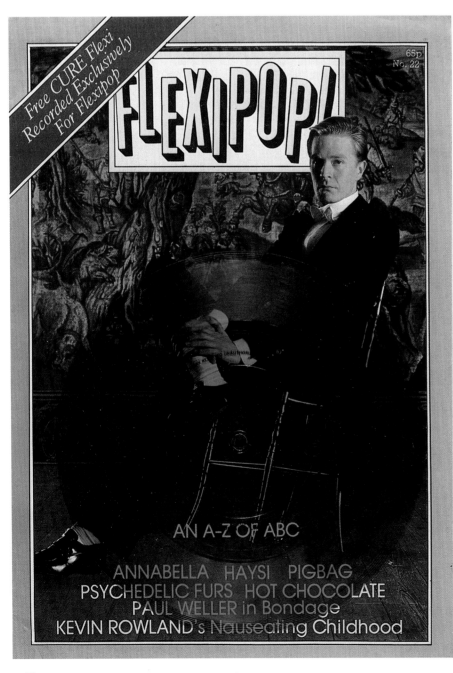

JAPANESE WHISPERS

UK RELEASE – DECEMBER, 1983
LP FIX M 8
Cassette FIXMC 8
CD 817470–2

Line up:
Robert Smith,
Laurence Tolhurst,
Andy Anderson,
Phil Thornalley,
Steve Goulding

Side One
Let's Go To Bed
The Dream
Just One Kiss
The Upstairs Room

Side Two
The Walk
Speak My Language
Lament
The Lovecats

JAPANESE WHISPERS
JAPANESE
VAP (35111–25)
This Japanese issue was released in 1984, a year later than in the UK. It included a Japanese lyrics insert with a large colour picture of The Cure. The titles on the sleeve were arranged slightly differently on pressings from South Africa (POLY 3519) also released in 1984, USA (SIRE 1-25076), France (POLYDOR 817470-1) and UK (FIXM 8). Not released until 1988 and differing from any other release of 'Japanese Whispers' was the Uruguayan issue (POLYDOR 817470-1). This sleeve was completely different with a picture of The Cure taken from the 1987 Kissing tour programme, replacing the standard sleeve design. The tracks remained unchanged.

LET'S GO TO BED
UK release – November, 1982
'Let's Go To Bed' was the first in the trilogy of singles, sometimes referred to as the Fantasy singles. Before this release there was disagreement between Chris Parry and The Cure who had reservations about 'Let's Go To Bed' as the A side and whether or not to release it under the name of The Cure at all. The sleeve was not a Parched Art design.
UK 7'' (FICS 17) 'Let's Go To Bed' b/w 'Just One Kiss'.

The A and B sides of all 7'' and 12'' releases remain the same as the UK unless noted.

Inscriptions in the run-off groove of this pressing read, side A 'Three for a girl', side B, 'Seven for a secret'. These were both lines from the Magpie nursery rhyme.

The UK 12'' (FICSX 17) had just two tracks featuring extended remixes of both 'Let's Go To Bed' b/w 'Just One Kiss'.

The run-off groove reads, side A 'But if one green bottle should accidentally fall', side B 'The Queen of Siam in my arms', which is a line from 'Just One Kiss'.

A promotional pressing of the 12'' was issued, but this had three tracks and only a plain white sleeve, (CUREX 1) 'Let's Go To Bed' (extended) b/w 'Let's Go To Bed' and 'Just One Kiss'. (extended). Its labels were the 1&2 promo type.

Spanish copies of the 7'' (2059 582) and 12'' (2141 682) had Spanish titles on the sleeve (VAMOS A LA CAMA). Misprinted credits on the label read Smith/Tolkhurst.

One sided 7'' acetate from 1982.

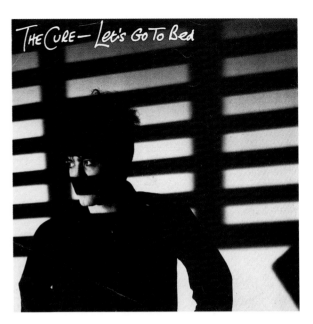

LET'S GO TO BED
USA

'Let's Go To Bed' was the first single released in the US. It was originally on licence from Fiction to be distributed by Important Records as a 12", with the same catalogue number, tracks and almost identical label as the UK 12" (FICSX 17). This US pressing, although it appears to be on completely black standard vinyl was actually pressed on a very dark purple vinyl. This goes totally unnoticed unless held up to the light. It is unclear if all copies are like this or just some of them. Strangely, the A side has a different message in its run-off groove reading "But if one green bottle should accidently rise". This release is one of the very few pressings outside the UK to have messages in its run-off groove.

For promotional use Fiction sent a small number of copies of the UK three track promo 12" (CUREX 1) to Important, which they distributed in a picture sleeve with a biography of The Cure and a letter from Important Records. Note the slightly larger picture on the sleeve.

Important's affiliation with Fiction was short lived. Sire Records took over releasing the single on 7" and 12" and widely distributed a double A sided 7" promo (PRO-S-2022) in the US that featured mono and stereo versions. It was also released on Sire in Australia and New Zealand, territories not covered by Polydor. 'Let's Go To Bed' reached number six in the US national chart.

this poster free when you buy the new cure 7" "the walk"

THE WALK B/W THE UPSTAIRS ROOM

FRENCH PROMOTIONAL ONLY 7"
POLYDOR (815 144–7)
'The Walk' was not released as a 7" single in France, but it was pressed as a promotional only 7" b/w 'The Upstairs Room'. This is a unique coupling of these two tracks and is a particularly rare pressing. 'The Upstairs Room' does not appear on any other 7". It was distributed with a French Polydor promo sleeve. Note 'Echantillon Gratuit Ne Peut Etre Vendu' on the label, meaning 'Promotional Only Record Not For Sale'.

THE WALK

UK release – July, 1983
UK 7" (FICS 18)
'The Walk' b/w 'The Dream'
This was the first single to be released in the UK on a multiplicity of editions. The sleeve was a Parched Art design. One sided posters were originally given away free with the standard 7" issue of 'The Walk'. The A and B side tracks remain the same on all 7" releases unless noted. In the UK it exists with three different labels.

Two limited editions were also released. The first was a 7" poster sleeve (FICS 18) unfolding with the same picture inside as the free poster. Later, a 7" picture disc (FICSP 18) was issued in a clear sleeve, both stills were from the video for the single. This was the first picture disc released by The Cure.

Note the translated titles, '*El Paseo*,' of this Spanish copy (813715–7). Unusual mispressings can be found of this issue. The A side states 'The Walk' on the label and has the A side matrix number in the run-off groove, but plays the B side track 'The Dream' and vice versa on the other side. Another pressing worth noting is the Dutch 7'' (Polydor 813715–7) as it has a larger picture of the fly on the sleeve.

THE WALK 12''

The 12'' of the 'The Walk' was released with a number of track variations. In the UK it was issued as a four track 12'' (FICSX 18) with 'The Upstairs Room' and 'The Dream' b/w 'The Walk' and 'Lament'. Promo copies were issued in a plain title stickered sleeve.

In other countries it was released as a six track mini LP with the previous single tracks 'Let's Go To Bed' and 'Just One Kiss' in addition to the four UK tracks.

The French pressing (810 752–1) includes the 7'' version of 'Let's Go To Bed' and 'Just One Kiss'. This was issued with two different labels, some red and others with picture labels.

Dutch copies (810752–1) include the 12'' extended version of 'Let's Go To Bed' and the 7'' version of 'Just One Kiss'.

In the US Sire Records released 'The Walk' as a mini LP (1–23928) and on cassette (4–23928), both including the 7'' version of 'Let's Go To Bed' and the 12'' extended version of 'Just One Kiss'. Sire also released this mini LP in Canada, Australia and New Zealand.

UK PROMO

UK

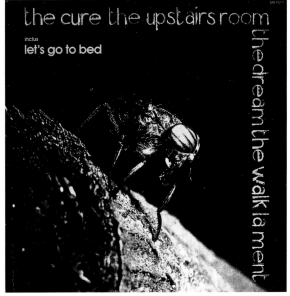

FRENCH

USA

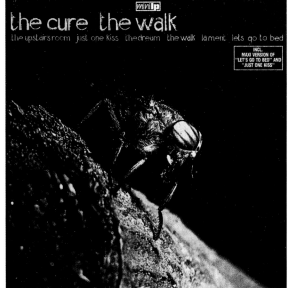

DUTCH

43

THE LOVECATS

UK release – October, 1983
This was the last of the three so-called Fantasy singles and was more commercially successful in the UK than 'Let's Go To Bed' and 'The Walk'. The A and B sides remained the same on all 7'' releases unless noted.

UK 7'' (FICS 19) 'The Lovecats' b/w 'Speak My Language'.

This was pressed with paper and injection mould labels. Scarce Irish pressings (FICS 19) were issued with red Polydor labels and Polydor sleeves.

Slightly later, a limited edition 7'' picture disc (FICSP 19) was released in the UK with a clear plastic sleeve. The pictures on each side of the record were from the video for the single.

Also worth noting are the many double A side promos that were issued in the US in addition to the standard release of 'The Lovecats' (SIRE 7–29376). These had no picture sleeves.

The sleeve of the Spanish 7'' (Polydor 815570–7) appeared with translated titles, 'Amor de Gatos.'

The UK 12'' (FICSX 19) features an extended version of 'The Lovecats' b/w 'Speak My Language' and 'Mr. Pink Eyes' as an extra track.

Mispressed copies of the US 12'' (SIRE 0–20161) can be found with the B side mastered at the wrong speed which results in 'Speak My Language' and 'Mr. Pink Eyes' playing too fast. These copies are impossible to recognise unless heard. Although unclear, it is thought only the first early pressings were like this. Worth noting is a 12'' pressing that was distributed in the Philippines (Polydor EP–PRO 8420) and issued with a picture sleeve.

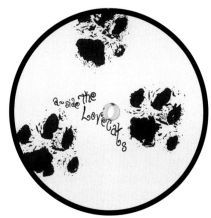

THE LOVECATS
b/w SPEAK MY LANGUAGE
SOUTH AFRICAN
POLYDOR (PS 8046)
Released 1984
Several months later in 1984 a
rare 7" pressing of 'The Lovecats'
was released in South Africa on
Polydor and distributed by
Trutone Music. This was the first
single in South Africa by The Cure.
It was issued with a picture sleeve
with a slight difference on the
border on the reverse side
although some copies, if found,
are without this picture sleeve.
In the same year, a South African
pressing of 'Japanese Whispers'
(Poly 3519) was released.

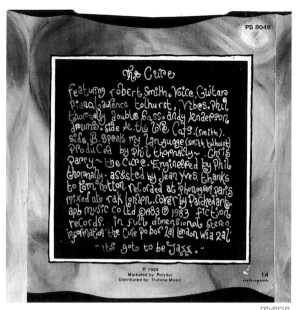

reverse

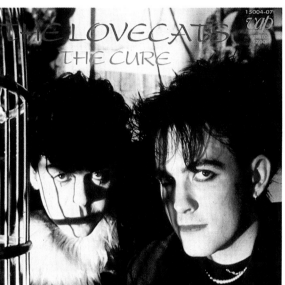

reverse

THE LOVECATS
b/w THE WALK
JAPANESE 7"
VAP (15004–07)
Released 1984
'The Lovecats' was The Cure's
second single in Japan. It was not
released until 1984 (the same
year that The Cure first toured
Japan and when three LPs were
released there), and was only
released as a 7". This pressing
replaces the original UK B side
('Speak My Language') with 'The
Walk' and is the only release with
this different sleeve. Often going
unnoticed are the repeated
mistakes in the lyrics to 'The
Lovecats' on the reverse of the
sleeve. Misprinted lyrics recur on
later Japanese releases.

Although a reasonably scarce
pressing, much rarer are the
white label promo copies that
were distributed. They were
issued with picture sleeves but
had orange and white inner
sleeves instead of black and white.
Note the Japanese writing on the
label meaning 'Sample Disc'.

Promo copy

THE GLOVE
BLUE SUNSHINE

UK RELEASE – AUGUST, 1983
LP   SHE LP 2
Cassette   SHEMC 2
CD   815 019–2

Line up:
Robert Smith,
Steve Severin,
Jeanette Landray.

Side One
Like An Animal
Looking Glass Girl
Sex-Eye-Make-Up
Mr. Alphabet Says
A Blues In Drag

Side Two
Punish Me With Kisses
This Green City
Orgy
Perfect Murder
Relax

The Glove was a studio project between Robert Smith and Steve Severin, and released from these recordings was the album 'Blue Sunshine' and two UK only singles, each on the Wonderland label. The name 'The Glove' was thought up by Steve Severin, who with Robert Smith was also involved in the design of the three sleeves with Da Gama. This was a group of five artists led by Alex McDowall, who also worked as the art director with Tim Pope on a few videos for The Cure. The recurring spiral on each of the sleeves was an idea of 'The Glove', taken from an episode of *The Avengers* about a hypnotic spiralling tunnel and it was also The Glove who were responsible for the characters on the album's sleeve.

After a long search for a singer by Robert Smith and Steve Severin, which included an advert on the *John Peel Show* for a vocalist, they eventually decided on Jeanette Landray, who sings on all but five of 'The Glove' tracks. Andy Anderson also features on the album.

LIKE AN ANIMAL
b/w MOUTH TO MOUTH
7''(SHE 3)
UK release – August, 1983
'Like An Animal' was the first
single by 'The Glove'. A limited
supply of posters was given away
with both the 7'' (SHE 3) and 12''
(SHEX 3) copies. Most copies of
the 7'' were pressed with paper
labels and issued with an unusual
hole in the centre of the sleeve,
others were pressed with injection
mould labels and issued without a
hole in the sleeve.

Inscriptions in the run-off
groove read: side A, 'What's
The Plan Mac?' and side B,
'The Plan Is This John'. These
were phrases often used by
Robert Smith's two nephews
and became a bit of an 'in joke'
between Robert Smith and
Steve Severin. Approximately
ten 7'' test pressings of this single
were produced.

BLUE SUNSHINE
JAPANESE
POLYDOR (28MM 0315)
'Blue Sunshine' was the only LP
released by 'The Glove'. No
other finished Glove recordings
remain that were not released.
The Japanese pressing (Polydor
28MM 0315) which Robert
Smith was once noted as saying
he didn't think existed, was
released in late November, 1983,
and is no doubt the most scarce
of all the releases of 'Blue
Sunshine'. Much rarer though,
is this white label promo copy.
Note the Japanese writing on the
label meaning 'Sample Disc –
Not For Sale'.

Commercial copies have red
Polydor labels. Both include a
lyric sheet in English and Japanese
and a Japanese biography. This
album was not released on cassette in Japan and was not
released in Europe until several
months later in 1984.

Test Pressing

**LIKE AN ANIMAL (CLUB,
WHAT CLUB? MIX) B/W
LIKE AN ANIMAL AND
MOUTH TO MOUTH**
12" (SHEX 3)
In addition to the two 7'' tracks,
the 12'' (SHEX 3) included an
extended version of 'Like An
Animal (Club, What Club? Mix)'.
Note the small differences in this
sleeve from the 7'', the yellow
and blue spiral is inversed and
the centre spiral and red dots
are different.

Promotional copies were
distributed in a plain sleeve with
a title sticker. The messages in the
run-off groove read, side A 'So
Anyway, There I Was', and side B
'But Everything Was A Dream'.

PUNISH ME WITH KISSES
B/W THE TIGHTROPE

7" (SHE 5)

UK release – November, 1983
'Punish Me With Kisses' was
released only as a 7" and was
pressed with paper labels. It was
remixed by Mike Hedges and is
slightly shorter than the version
on 'Blue Sunshine'.

The inscriptions in the run-off
groove read: side A, 'Please
Don't Interrupt Whilst I'm
Soliloquizing', side B, 'Laughter,
There Was Never Laughter'.

These are two lines spoken by
Vincent Price and Christopher
Lee in *The House Of The Long
Shadows*, one of many films seen
by Robert Smith and Steve
Severin during 'The Glove'
recordings. No more than ten
test pressings were made of
this single, which although only
released in the UK was actually
pressed in France by Mayking
Records.

Test Pressing

First ever collaboration between Robert Smith of The Cure and Steve Severin of Siouxsie and the Banshees. A classic 1983 recording issued for the first time in the U.S.

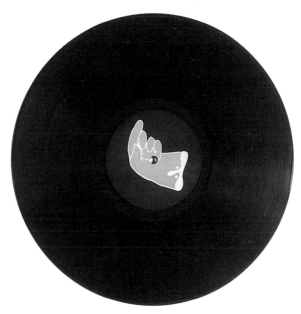

In 1990, 'Blue Sunshine' was released on CD (815019–2) and included the three B sides 'Mouth To Mouth', 'The Tightrope' and 'Like An Animal (extended)' as bonus tracks.

It was released for the first time in 1990 in the US on LP, CD and cassette and distributed by Rough Trade. The LP was issued on blue vinyl (RUS 85–1) which was widely available. The CD (RUS 85–2) was issued in standard USA 12'' long box packaging with a slightly different design on the disc to the UK.

The Japanese CD (POCP–1885) was issued as part of Polydor Japan's budget priced 'Nice Price' series.

THE TOP

UK RELEASE – MAY, 1984
LP FIXS 9
Cassette FIXSC 9
CD 821136–2

Line up:
Robert Smith,
Laurence Tolhurst,
Andy Anderson,
Porl Thompson,

Side One
Shake Dog Shake
Bird Mad Girl
Wailing Wall
Give Me It
Dressing Up

Side Two
The Caterpillar
Piggy In The Mirror
The Empty World
Bananafishbones
The Top

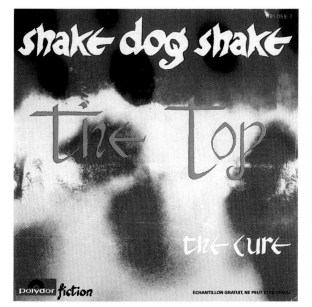

reverse

SHAKE DOG SHAKE
b/w THE TOP
FRENCH PROMOTIONAL
ONLY 7''
1984 POLYDOR (881 058-7)
This much talked about pressing
of 'Shake Dog Shake' b/w 'The
Top' is another unique record
from France. It was never
released commercially and exists
as a promotional pressing only;
approximately a few hundred
copies were pressed.

The colour picture sleeve
makes it particularly unusual
among other promotional only
pressings which are rarely distributed in anything other than a
plain sleeve. Some copies exist
with gold coloured injection
mould labels and were distributed
in plain sleeves. A four page
promo booklet was also produced
by Polydor France which featured
photos of The Cure and French
reviews from 1984. The cover
was the same design as the
'Shake Dog Shake' sleeve, only
a very small number of these
were issued.

Something often mentioned by
collectors, but very seldom seen
and possibly the most unusual
Cure promotional gimmick, is
the toy spinning top and snake,
distributed in the UK as a
promotion for 'The Top' LP.

The top and snake are func-
tional but bizarre: while the top
is spinning, the metal snake is
placed at the magnetic tip of the
spinning top, causing the snake to
dance forwards, backwards and
around. These were distributed
in several different colours, each
in a small packet.

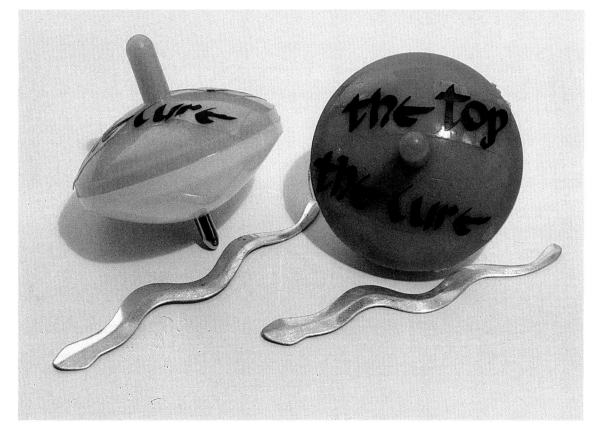

BIRD MAD GIRL
SHAKE DOG SHAKE
BANANAFISHBONES
(KAREN 1A) 1984
This 12" pressing was produced
purely for promotional use only
in the UK and issued as a pre-
release album sampler for 'The
Top'. It is a one sided pressing
playing at 33 1/3 rpm, the B side
is completely blank and none of
the three tracks was released
as a single. This is a very rare
pressing and most copies, if
found, have a plain black sleeve
with a title sticker. Other copies
were distributed with a white
sleeve that, as well as the title
sticker, depicts a small spinning
top logo on the front. In the past
the authenticity of this sleeve has
been doubted by some collectors
but it is definitely genuine and
was produced by Polydor specially
for this pressing.

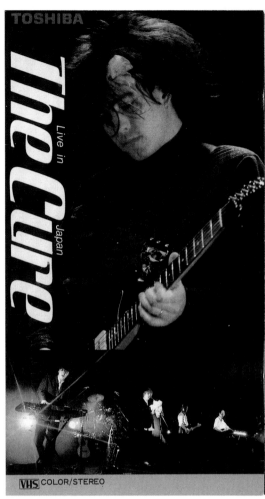

THE TOP
JAPANESE
VAP (35117–25)
Early copies of this Japanese
pressing included a large full
colour glossy poster of Robert
Smith and Laurence Tolhurst.

THE CURE LIVE IN JAPAN
TOSHIBA (VTS/M129VH)
NTSC system only.
'The Cure Live In Japan' is an
obscure and particularly odd
video . It was a Japanese production released exclusively in Japan
by Toshiba in 1985 and not by
the VAP label. This in fact was
the first ever official live video
of The Cure and is virtually
unheard of outside Japan, as very
little (if any) reference has ever
been made of to it in any book
or magazine.

It was filmed in Tokyo on the
last night of The Top tour in Japan
during October 1984 and
features rarely performed songs
such as 'Wailing Wall', 'The
Empty World', 'The Top' and
'The Caterpillar'. This was the
last time Andy Anderson played
with The Cure.

It also includes dressing room
footage, an interview with The
Cure, an appearance by Perry
Bamonte, the soundcheck and
after show film of Robert Smith
accepting flowers from fans. It is
unclear exactly when 'The Cure
Live In Japan' was deleted but it is
a unique video which is very
rarely, if ever, found.

THE CATERPILLAR

UK release – May, 1984

'The Caterpillar' was the only single released from The Top album.
UK 7'' (FICS 20) 'The Caterpillar' b/w 'Happy The Man'.
UK 12'' (FICSX 20) 'The Caterpillar' b/w 'Happy The Man and 'Throw Your Foot' as an extra track. These tracks remain the same on all releases of 'The Caterpillar'.

Most copies of the UK 7'' were pressed with paper labels, while others were pressed with injection mould labels, but are considerably less common. An additional 7'' was released as a limited edition picture disc.

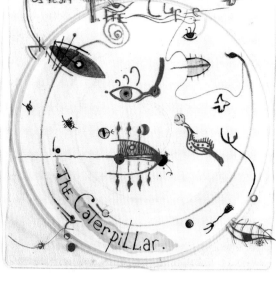

THE CATERPILLAR
b/w HAPPY THE MAN

UK 7'' PICTURE DISC (FICSP 20) Originally, Parched Art designed this record as a clear vinyl picture disc. But once they had made a mock-up design on clear vinyl, the idea was scrapped because the design on each side could be seen through the vinyl.

Subsequently it was released as a white picture disc in a clear plastic sleeve with an embossed design. Half of this design is on the front of the sleeve and half is on the reverse. So only when the record is out of the sleeve can the whole design be seen. Some copies included a titled sleeve sticker.

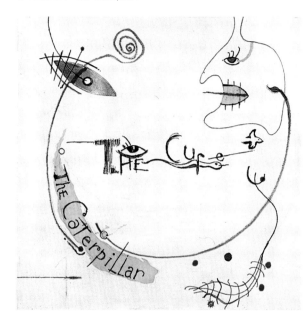

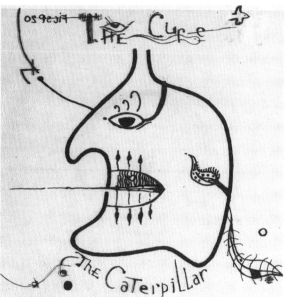

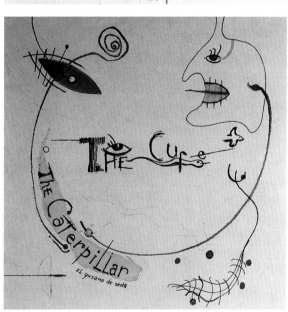

Note the translation of the title on the sleeve of the Spanish issue 7'' (821458–7), 12'' (821458 1). Worth noting is the Italian promo juke box pressing of 'The Caterpillar' (AS 5000 676) which was b/w A Different Artist. 'The Caterpillar' was also released in Ireland, Germany, Holland, France, Italy, Australia and New Zealand but was not released in the USA.

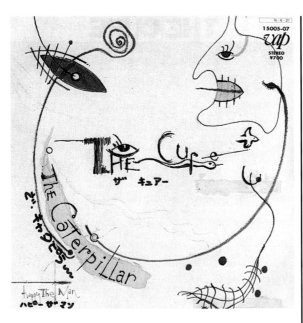

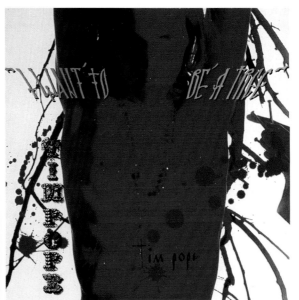

UK release – August, 1984

'I Want To Be A Tree' was written by Tim Pope and his school friend Charlie Gray when they were both only 15 years old.

Later, in about 1984, it was recorded as a joke for amusement purposes and was not intended as a single. Tim Pope sang whilst Charlie Gray played all the instruments. A video film was made, this included amongst others, The Cure, Siouxsie and The Banshees and Soft Cell. It was shown only once on the *Old Grey Whistle Test*.

Although Tim Pope received several offers to release it as a single, it was Fiction who decided to release it in the UK only, as a 7'' and 12'' single. It was re-recorded, this time with The Cure. Robert Smith played guitar and sang backing vocals, Porl Thompson played sax on '(Elephant) Song' and Lol Tolhurst and Andy Anderson also played. A second video was made, this time with Tim Pope on his own and as a tree.

The songs on the B side '(Elephant) Song' and 'The Double Crossing of Two Faced Fred' were written even earlier, when Tim Pope was about 12 years old.

7'' (FICS 21) 'I Want To Be A Tree' b/w 'The Double Crossing Of Two Faced Fred'. Inscriptions in the run-off groove read: side A, 'If Trees Grow In The Forest......' Side B reads, 'Pap Grow In The Trees.....'.

12'' (FICSX 21) 'I Want To Be A Tree' b/w 'The Double Crossing Of Two Faced Fred' and '(Elephant) Song' as an extra track. The inscription in the B-side run-off groove reads, 'A Smith Is As Good As A Smile', an obvious reference to Robert Smith. There is no inscription on the A-side.

The sleeve, a Da Gama design, differs slightly for each pressing. Also, the 7'' sleeve has the lyrics to the B side on the reverse, continuing on to the label. The 12'' has lyrics to '(Elephant) Song'.

THE CATERPILLAR
b/w HAPPY THE MAN
JAPANESE 7''

VAP (15005–07)

'The Caterpillar' was one of the few singles by The Cure to be released in Japan, it was only released as a 7'' and has English and Japanese lyrics on the reverse. This particular white label promo copy has hand written Japanese titles on the sleeve and is a far rarer copy than the standard Japanese issue (15005–07) which is also scarce.

CONCERT

UK RELEASE – OCTOBER, 1984
LP FIXH 10
Cassette FIXHC 10
CD 823682-2

Line up:
Robert Smith,
Porl Thompson,
Andy Anderson,
Phil Thornalley,
Laurence Tolhurst

Side One
Shake Dog Shake
Primary
Charlotte Sometimes
The Hanging Garden
Give Me It

Side Two
The Walk
One Hundred Years
A Forest
10.15 Saturday Night
Killing An Arab

57

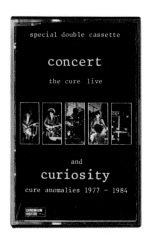

CURIOSITY
(FIXHC 10)
The cassette of 'Concert' was issued as a double play cassette. This featured 10 extra live tracks on the B side, under the title of 'Curiosity'. Amongst these live songs were the unreleased 'Heroin Face', 'All Mine' and 'Forever'. Each of the bonus live tracks came from Robert Smith's own collection of taped performances.'Curiosity' is only available on the cassette of 'Concert'.

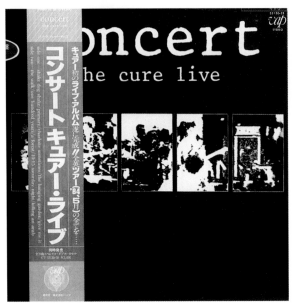

A FOREST (LIVE) b/w SHAKE DOG SHAKE (LIVE)
FRENCH PROMOTIONAL ONLY 7'' POLYDOR (881 622–7)
Again a unique 7'' record from France, it was pressed as a promotion for, and as a possible single from the album 'Concert'. It features a unique coupling of two songs from the album. 'A Forest (live)' b/w 'Shake Dog Shake (live)' was never released and like previous French 7'' records has remained as a very rare promotional only pressing. It was distributed in a French Polydor promo sleeve.

CONCERT
JAPANESE
VAP (35130–25)
This scarce Japanese promo copy of 'Concert' is an example of the white labels VAP used and how they varied from commercial copies. Note the small red promo sticker on the sleeve. An insert is included with lyrics and a biography. 'Concert' was the first LP that was released in Brazil.

EXCERPT
A FOREST (LIVE)
b/w PRIMARY (LIVE)
1984

'Excerpt' was released only as a
12'' featuring two live tracks from
the album 'Concert'. 'A Forest'
features as the A side, but
despite the previous French
promo 7'', it featured 'Primary'
as the B side instead of 'Shake
Dog Shake'.

   Polydor released it only in
Germany, France and Holland.
German (881448–1) and Dutch
(881448–1) issues are more
common than the French pressing (881448–1) and were available
on import in the UK. Note only
the French issue has Fiction,
Polydor and Maxi 45 Tours in
each corner of the sleeve.

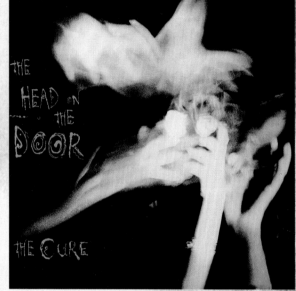

THE HEAD ON THE DOOR

UK RELEASE – AUGUST 1985
LP FIXH 11
Casette FIXHC 11
CD 827231-2

Line-up:
Robert Smith,
Laurence Tolhurst,
Porl Thompson,
Simon Gallup
Boris Williams.

Side One
In Between Days
Kyoto Song
The Blood
Six Different Ways
Push

Side Two
The Baby Screams
Close To Me
A Night Like This
Screw
Sinking

A page from the booklet.

THE HEAD ON THE DOOR

JAPANESE
VAP (35151–27)
Early copies of this Japanese issue of 'The Head On The Door' included a special large 8 page full colour picture booklet of The Cure, in addition to the biography and illustrated discography normally included. On the reverse of the obi is an advert for 'The Tea Party' video.

The unusual inscription '50 Times A Night' is found in the A side run off groove of UK copies of the LP and on the B side, 'They Do It.' It is referring to the tiger.

THE HEAD ON THE DOOR

ARGENTINIAN
POLYDOR (827231–1)
Released 1986
No LPs by The Cure were available in Argentina until 1986 when 'The Head On The Door' was released as the first. Strangely, it was issued with the sleeve design of 'In Between Days', replacing the normal sleeve design created by Parched Art from a photograph of Robert Smith's sister Janet. The lyrics and a picture of the 'Close To Me' sleeve are on the reverse. This particular example is a promo copy stating *Difusion-venta prohibida* on the label and a translation of the album's title ('*Cabeza contra la puerta*').

Polydor also released 'Standing On A Beach' in this year and in 1987, 'Seventeen Seconds' (29073), 'Faith' (29065), 'Pornography' (29059), 'The Top' (29053) and 'Concert' (27387) were all released for the first time in Argentina.

IN BETWEEN DAYS

UK release – July, 1985
UK 7"(FICS 22) 'In Between Days' b/w 'The Exploding Boy' This issue was pressed with paper labels and with injection mould labels in blue and silver.

No limited editions were released of 'In Between Days'. The A and B side tracks remain the same as the UK 7" and 12" pressings on all releases unless noted. The title 'The Exploding Boy' was once a possible title for 'The Head On The Door'.

UK 12" (FICSX 22) 'In Between Days' b/w 'The Exploding Boy' and with 'A Few Hours After This' as an extra track. Promo copies (FICSX 22 DJ) have the same tracks and plain sleeves.

'In Between Days' was the first of the 12" Brazilian promo pressings by The Cure (Polydor 2801 120). It featured a totally different artist on the B side and had just a plain titled sleeve.

In October 1988, 'In Between Days' along with 'Close To Me', 'Catch' and 'Why Can't I Be You?' was released on CDV. It features the audio and video of 'In Between Days' and audio tracks, of 'The Exploding Boy', 'A Few Hours After This' and two live tracks from 'The Cure In Orange', 'Six Different Ways' and 'Push' (080182 – 2) (also on the 'Why Can't I Be You?' double pack 7").

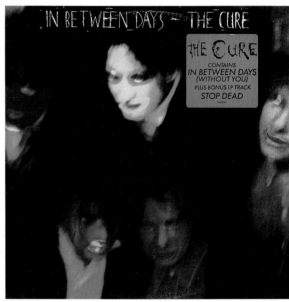

IN BETWEEN DAYS

US AND CANADA

The American and Canadian releases of 'In Between Days' feature a number of variations not found on any other release.

The 7" pressing US (7–69604), Canada (9696047) both feature 'Stop Dead' on the B side instead of 'The Exploding Boy'. The sleeve includes the B side titles on the front. Worth noting is that two different promo copies of 'In Between Days' were distributed by Elektra in the US . One was a double A side of the single version (7–69604) and the other was a double A side edited 2:16 version of 'In Between Days' (7–69604C). Both were issued in large numbers and with Elektra sleeves.

The 12" pressing, US (0–66882), Canada (9668820) feature an exclusive extended version of 'In Between Days' with 'Stop Dead' on the B side and 'In Between Days' (single version) on the A side.

These releases were issued with title stickers on the sleeve. Promo copies (ED 5085) were issued with standard sleeves and the same tracks.

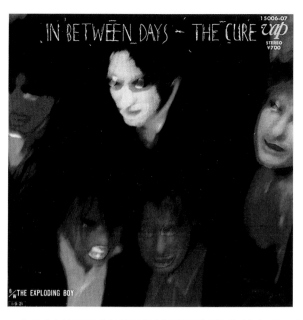

IN BETWEEN DAYS b/w THE EXPLODING BOY
JAPANESE 7''
VAP (15006–07)
It is particularly unusual that a small Japanese company like VAP would produce a special promotional folder for a single.

This housed a promo copy of 'In Between Days' (15006–07) and gives details and release dates for 'In Between Days' and 'The Head On The Door'. It talks about The Cure and gives a brief Japanese discography, no more than 100 of these would have been made by VAP.

Promo copy

CLOSE TO ME

UK Release – September, 1985
This single version of 'Close To Me' was a remix of the version on 'The Head On The Door' and was the first time two singles had been released from the same album. Various changes of B sides and small differences in sleeve design occur amongst foreign releases of 'Close To Me'.

UK 7'' (FICS 23) 'Close To Me' b/w 'A Man Inside My Mouth'. This was pressed with paper and injection mould labels. A limited edition of the 7'' was issued in the UK with a fold out poster sleeve (FICSG 23).

UK 12'' (FICSX 23) 'Close To Me' (extended) b/w 'A Man Inside My Mouth' and 'Stop Dead'. Promo copies (FICSX 23 DJ) featured the same tracks and some included a poster. This 12'' was for a short time available as a bonus disc, shrink-wrapped with UK copies of 'The Head On The Door'.

Spanish and Italian pressings have the same tracks as the UK, but differ slightly, in that the Spanish 7'' (883361–7) has translated sleeve titles, and the sleeve of the Italian 7'' (883361–7) is the same on both sides. In addition to this a promo jukebox single (5000 713) was also issued in Italy.

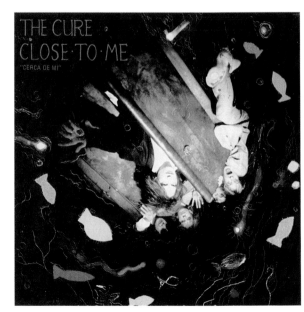

CLOSE TO ME (EXTENDED)
b/w A MAN INSIDE MY MOUTH AND STOP DEAD

JAPANESE 12''

VAP (35153-12)

Not released as a 7'' in Japan, 'Close To Me' was only released on 12'', this was the first and only 12'' by The Cure on the VAP label. It included a picture insert with Japanese and English lyrics. The back of the obi included an advert for 'The Tea Party' video, white label promo copies were also distributed. It has the same three tracks as the UK 12''. Consequently, the 7'' version of 'Close To Me' was unavailable in Japan until 1986 on 'Standing On A Beach'.

HALF AN OCTOPUSS

10'' (FICST 23)

A four track 10'' pressing with the title 'Half An Octopuss' was issued in the UK as a limited edition. Not all copies were issued with a sticker. It featured 'Close To Me' (7'' version), both B side tracks and 'New Day' as an extra track.

The 1988 CDV released in the UK and Europe of 'Close To Me' (080 180-2) had a similar track listing to 'Half An Octopus'. Additional tracks, to the video for the single ,were 'Close To Me' (extended), 'A Man Inside My Mouth', 'Stop Dead' and 'New Day'.

CLOSE TO ME
b/w SINKING 7''

The American and Canadian release is very different from any other pressing of the single. Instead of the single version of 'Close To Me' (3.39) Elektra Records released the LP version of 'Close To Me' (3.23) as the single in the US and Canada.

Another unusual difference was the LP track 'Sinking' featured as the B side on both releases, US (7–69551) and Canadian

(96 95517). This is the only pressing with 'Sinking' on the B side. Both releases had Elektra sleeves.

Promotional copies were issued in both countries, large numbers of double A side pressings were distributed in the US (7–69551). Scarce Canadian promos featured the same tracks as the commercial release: 'Close To Me' b/w 'Sinking' (96 95517).

QUADPUSS
A NIGHT LIKE THIS AND NEW DAY b/w
CLOSE TO ME (EXTENDED) AND A MAN INSIDE MY MOUTH

The American and Canadian equivalent to the 12'' pressing of 'Close To Me' was 'Quadpuss', a 12'' variation of the UK 'Half An Octopus'. It was not released until 1986.

Quadpuss does not include 'Stop Dead', but presents 'A Night Like This' as a main title of the record and which at one point was a possible single, with a video for the track being made to accompany this release. The only difference between the Canadian (9668560) and the USA (066856) issues is the label and the colour of titles on the reverse of the sleeve. Quadpuss was not released anywhere else.

A rare one sided 7'' test pressing for the US single

A NIGHT LIKE THIS b/w
A NIGHT LIKE THIS

USA PROMOTIONAL 12'' ELEKTRA (ED 5130)

Elektra issued a large number of double sided 12'' pressings of 'A Night Like This' for promotional use only in the USA. It was issued in 1985 before the release of 'Quadpuss' with a plain Elektra sleeve. 'A Night Like This' was also included on an Elektra promo cassette issued in Canada (SAMC 51) Again promoting 'A Night Like This' as the main title on 'Quadpuss' and plans for a possible single release.

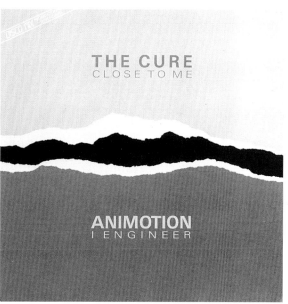

AMIGA QUARTETT CLOSE TO ME (LP VERSION) AND STOP DEAD B/W A MAN INSIDE MY MOUTH AND NEW DAY

AMIGA (5 56 195)

This 7'' of 'Close To Me' was released under the title of 'Amiga Quartett'. It is a unique pressing from former East Germany which was not released until 1988 by the official East German state label Amiga, on licence from Metronome Music. It has the same tracks as 'Half An Octopus', except for the LP version of 'Close To Me' instead of the single version. Copies of this record were more commonly found in the UK after the unification of East and West Germany. A small number of white label copies were pressed for radio use.

CLOSE TO ME

BRAZILIAN PROMO 12''
MERCURY (2801143)

This 12'' promo of 'Close To Me' was not issued until 1986 and is typical of the way Brazilian promos often present two different artists on the same record.

On the A-side it has the LP version of 'Close To Me'. On the reverse side of the sleeve, it talks briefly about the success of 'Concert' and 'The Head On The Door'. Brazilian 12'' singles are pressed purely for promotional use by radio stations (to promote the present LP). No 7'' or 12'' Cure singles are pressed for commercial sale in Brazil.

It is very unusual for a B side track of a single to appear on a compilation album in preference to the A side, but in this case 'A Man Inside My Mouth' was included on this seven track Greek compilation LP in 1986 called 'The Disc of Pop and Rock' (Polydor 819608–1). It is the only other record where this track can be found other than the formats released for the single.

THE CURE TEA PARTY

VHS (VAP 66011–68)
BETTA (VAP 66012–68)
This video 'The Cure Tea Party' is somewhat of an anomaly. It was released by VAP exclusively in Japan and like the previous 'The Cure Live In Japan' is a video to which very little reference has been made in any other country.

It is a compilation of just nine of The Cure's videos. 'Play For Today', 'Primary', 'The Hanging Garden', 'Let's Go To Bed', 'The Walk', 'The Lovecats', 'The Caterpillar', 'In Between Days' and 'Close To Me'.

Effectively it was the very first time that these videos were commercially available, 'The Cure Tea Party' was released in 1985 a year before the very much wider release of the 1986 compilation 'Staring At The Sea'.

VAP released 'Tea Party' on VHS and Bettamax formats; both were essentially small releases and were deleted within two years and for this reason it is a very rare video.

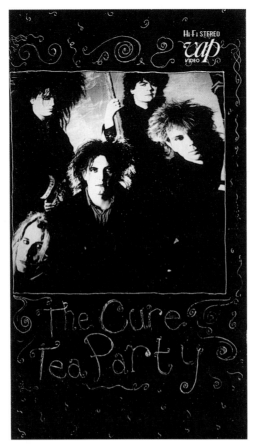
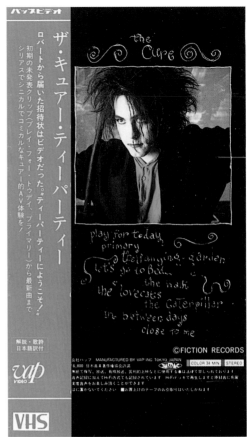

reverse

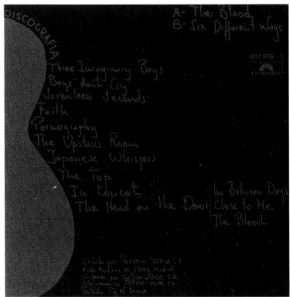

reverse

THE BLOOD b/w SIX DIFFERENT WAYS

SPANISH 7'' 1986.
POLYDOR (883 836–7)
This record was pressed only in Spain and features a unique coupling of 'The Blood' with 'Six Different Ways' on the B side. It exists only as a 7'' pressing and was not issued until 1986, after 'The Head On The Door', 'In Between Days' and 'Close To Me'. The brief discography on the reverse of the sleeve lists 'The Blood' as a single, clearly indicating that it was intended as a third release although it is unclear whether or not it was released commercially. It is thought only 300-400 copies were pressed and used as promotional discs, although this is not stated on the label or sleeve. Polydor Spain created the sleeve design and a video for the single featuring two flamenco dancers. It did not feature The Cure, nor was it connected with Tim Pope.

In the same year, 1986, 'The Blood' was included on a scarce Argentinian promotional 12'' (POLYDOR 0000 529) that was issued by Polydor to clubs and DJs and which included five other artists.

THE CURE · STANDING ON A BEACH · THE SINGLES

A
THE CURE
STANDING ON A BEACH · THE SINGLES

KILLING AN ARAB
(SMITH/TOLHURST/DEMPSEY)
FIXH12　BOYS DON'T CRY　33RPM
(SMITH/TOLHURST/DEMPSEY)
JUMPING SOMEONE ELSE'S TRAIN
(SMITH/TOLHURST/DEMPSEY)
©FICTION RECORDS 1986　℗FICTION RECORDS 1986
A FOREST
(SMITH/TOLHURST/GALLUP/HARTLEY)
PRIMARY
(SMITH/TOLHURST/GALLUP)
CHARLOTTE SOMETIMES
(SMITH/TOLHURST/GALLUP)
THE HANGING GARDEN
(SMITH/TOLHURST/GALLUP)

ORIGINAL SOUND RECORDING MADE BY FICTION RECORDS.
ALL TRACKS PERFORMED BY THE CURE.
ALL TRACKS PUBLISHED BY APB MUSIC CO. LTD

STANDING ON A BEACH

UK RELEASE – MAY, 1986
LP FIXH 12
Cassette FIXHC 12
CD 829239–2
'Staring at the Sea'

Line up:
Robert Smith,
Simon Gallup,
Porl Thompson,
Boris Williams,
Laurence Tolhurst

Side One
Killing An Arab
Boys Don't Cry
Jumping Someone Else's Train
A Forest
Primary
Charlotte Sometimes
The Hanging Garden

Side Two
Let's Go To Bed
The Walk
The Lovecats
The Caterpillar
In Between Days
Close To Me

STANDING ON A BEACH
JAPANESE
VAP (35159–25)

'Standing On A Beach' was the last album released in Japan on the VAP label before The Cure switched to Polydor Japan. On the back of the obi is an advert for 'Boys Don't Cry' and the CD and cassette of 'Standing On A Beach'.

Pressings of this LP from Argentina, Brazil, the Philippines, Israel and Spain all had single pocket sleeves and not gatefold sleeves. Elektra Records placed a disclaimer sticker referring to 'Killing An Arab' on the sleeve of USA and Canadian releases.

The CD of this album was released under the name 'Staring At The Sea' and included four tracks not on the LP, '10.15 Saturday Night', 'Play For Today', 'Other Voices' and 'A Night Like This'.

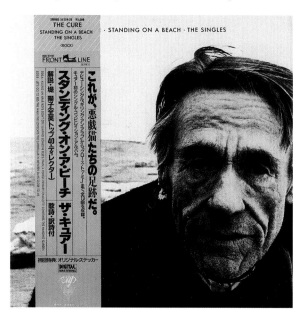

The song KILLING AN ARAB has absolutely no racist overtones whatsoever. It is a song which decries the existence of all prejudice and consequent violence. The Cure condemn its use in furthering anti-Arab feeling.

STANDING ON A BEACH
CASSETTE (FIXHC 12)

'Standing On A Beach' was issued as a double play cassette which included the 12 B side tracks that were not previously made available on any album. 'I'm Cold', 'Another Journey By Train', 'Descent', 'Splintered In Her Head', 'Mr Pink Eyes', 'Happy The Man', 'Throw Your Foot', 'The Exploding Boy', 'A Few Hours After This', 'A Man Inside My Mouth', 'Stop Dead' and 'New Day'. These extra B-side tracks were only available on the cassette of the album. Greek copies of this cassette (POLYDOR 829239-4) were issued without the track 'Happy The Man'.

In the Philippines only 'Standing On A Beach' was issued as an unusual two cassette package (POLYDOR 829239-4) with the B-side tracks on the additional cassette (829239-4/2).

STARING AT THE SEA
(PVC 3011M)
UK Release – May, 1986

'Staring At The Sea' was a retrospective compilation of home movie clips and all seventeen of The Cure's videos from 1979–1986. It was released to complement the 'Standing On A Beach' album. For the first time, videos had been specially made for the first three singles for inclusion on 'Staring At The Sea'. In Japan and the US 'Staring At The Sea' was available as a 12'' laser disc.

THE CURE IN ORANGE
POLYGRAM (0415542)
UK Release – November, 1987

A live production filmed specially by Tim Pope of The Cure's two night performance at the Roman Amphitheatre in Orange, France on the 9th and 10th August 1986. 'The Cure in Orange' was also released in October 1988 on 12'' laser disc.

BOYS DON'T CRY
(NEW VOICE NEW MIX)

UK Release – April, 1986
This was the main title released to promote 'Standing On A Beach'. In the UK and in most other countries it was the only single released to promote the album. It was a re-sung and re-mixed version of the original 1979 'Boys Don't Cry' single, although it is the original version that is on the 'Standing On A Beach' compilation and not the new version.

The two B side tracks were recorded in 1979 and were previously unreleased. The A and B sides remain the same as the UK pressings on all 7'' and 12'' releases unless noted.

UK 7'' (FICS 24) 'Boys Don't Cry' b/w 'Pillbox Tales'.

UK 12'' (FICSX 24) 'Boys Don't Cry (Extended Remix)' b/w 'Pillbox Tales' and 'Do the Hansa' as a bonus track.

12'' promo copies(FICSX 24DJ) were distributed in the UK. Some were in picture sleeves with a poster. Others were in a plain white sleeve with a special printed copy of a hand written letter by Robert Smith, explaining the single and the soon to be released 'Standing On A Beach'.

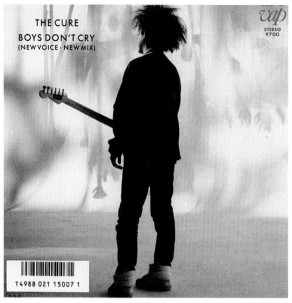

This was the last single in Japan on the VAP label. It was released only on 7'' and the sleeve, unlike previous releases, opens up with English and Japanese lyrics inside and a review of The Cure. White label promo copies were also issued.

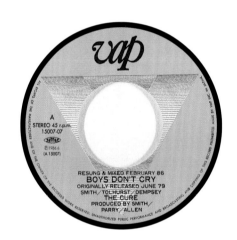

For the first time a single was issued in Uruguay and Argentina. Note the difference in the sleeve colour of the 12'' Uruguayan copy of 'Boys Don't Cry' (POLYDOR 22304). The Argentinian issue (POLYDOR 22304) had a picture on the reverse advertising 'Standing On A Beach' and 'The Head On the Door'. Also worth noting is a 12'' pressing that was issued in the Philippines (PRO 3754).

LET'S GO TO BED
b/w BOYS DON'T CRY

While 'Boys Don't Cry (Remix)' was being released in the UK and Europe, Elektra chose differently and re-released 'Let's Go To Bed' in the USA and Canada, but put 'Boys Don't Cry (Remix)' on the B side. Only the 7'' pressing USA (7–69537), Canada (9695377) had this sleeve design.

Two 7'' promo copies were issued in the USA, one a double A side pressing of 'Let's Go To Bed' (7–69537), the other a double B side pressing of 'Boys Don't Cry'(7–69537). Large numbers of each were distributed. Canadian promo copies (9695377) had the same A and B sides as the commercial issue.

The 12'' pressing, USA (0–29689) and Canadian (9296890) was released without the track 'Boys Don't Cry (Remix)' and was issued with the original 1982 sleeve design. It featured the same three tracks that were on the original UK promo 12'' (CUREX 1), 'Let's Go To Bed (Extended)' b/w 'Let's Go To Bed' and 'Just One Kiss (Extended)'.

Two 12'' promos were distributed in the USA. (ED 5146) 'Let's Go To Bed' b/w 'Let's Go To Bed (Extended)'. (ED 5175) 'Boys Don't Cry (Remix)' b/w 'Boys Don't Cry (Extended)'.

Less common was a one sided 12'' test pressing of 'Let's Go To Bed' , 7'' version (ED 5146) which was also distributed by Elektra for additional promotional use by radio stations.

THE CURE · LET'S GO TO BED

CHARLOTTE SOMETIMES
b/w SPLINTERED IN HER HEAD.

RE–ISSUE 1986
In addition to the 'Boys Don't Cry' single, 'Charlotte Sometimes' was re-issued in France and Germany on 7'' (885 356–7) and 12'' (885 356–1).

The A and B side tracks were the same as the original pressings. The German 12'' was re–issued with the same sleeve as the original UK 12'' and not the original super sound single sleeve design.

reverse

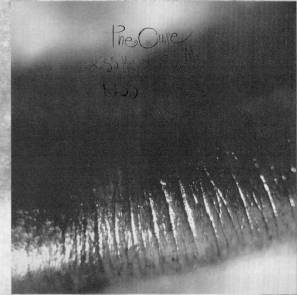

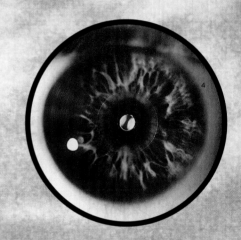

KISS ME, KISS ME, KISS ME

UK RELEASE – MAY, 1987
LP FIXH 13
Cassette FIXHC 13
CD 832 130–2

Line up:
Robert Smith,
Simon Gallup,
Porl Thompson,
Boris Williams,
Laurence Tolhurst

Side One
The Kiss
Catch
Torture
If Only Tonight We Could Sleep

Side Two
Why Can't I Be You?
How Beautiful You Are
The Snakepit
Hey You

Side Three
Just Like Heaven
All I Want
Hot Hot Hot!!!
One More Time
Like Cockatoos

Side Four
Icing Sugar
The Perfect Girl
A Thousand Hours
Shiver And Shake
Fight

KISS ME, KISS ME, KISS ME,
UK (FIXH 13)
Some UK copies of 'Kiss Me, Kiss Me, Kiss Me', were issued with an obi around the sleeve, a characteristic normally found only on Japanese pressings. These copies were available for a short time during the release of 'Catch'. An unknown number of mispressings of this UK. issue exist where side three plays side one.

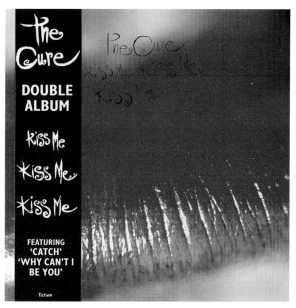

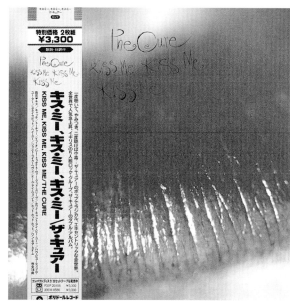

KISS ME, KISS ME, KISS ME,
LIMITED EDITION
(FIXHA 13)
UK release – December, 1987
This limited edition of 'Kiss Me, Kiss Me, Kiss Me' was released in December (the same month as the UK Kissing tour dates).

It was issued as a shrink wrapped package with a bonus orange vinyl 12'' in a clear plastic titled sleeve. This bonus record has a specially compiled collection of the previous five B side tracks, 'A Japanese Dream', 'Breathe' and 'A Chain Of Flowers' b/w 'Sugar Girl', 'Snow In Summer' and a new remixed version of 'Icing Sugar'.

Test pressings of this bonus 12'' record were pressed on black vinyl.

KISS ME, KISS ME, KISS ME,
JAPANESE
POLYDOR (33MM 0566/7)
'Kiss Me', was the last album by The Cure released on vinyl in Japan, and of all the different releases of the LP this Japanese pressing is particularly distinctive. It is the only release with a gate fold sleeve opening up with lyrics printed inside. A gatefold picture insert with Japanese lyrics and a biography is included. Note 'Sample Disc, Not for Sale' in Japanese on the label of this rare promotional copy. Worth noting is the rare Uruguayan pressing of 'Kiss Me' (Polydor 832132-1) which is a good example of the unconventional way in which South American countries sometimes released records. Instead of being sold as a double LP it was split and sold separately. Each record had a picture of The Cure on the reverse of the sleeve.

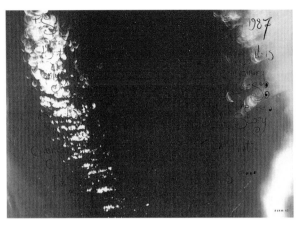

This large insert announcing the release of the book 'Ten Imaginary Years' came with both promotional copies and the very first issues of 'Kiss Me, Kiss Me, Kiss Me'.

KISS ME INTERVIEW DISC
(KSME 2)
On this interview disc, Robert Smith talks about songs from 'Kiss Me, Kiss Me, Kiss Me' and some of the ideas behind them. It was a promotional only pressing and again it had a special promo sleeve. The interview was recorded in Paris on April 14, 1987. This record was distributed only in the UK and included a transcript of the interview.

**KISS ME 12"
PROMOTIONAL ALBUM
SAMPLER** (KSME1)
This record features four songs from 'Kiss Me, Kiss Me, Kiss Me'. It was pressed for promotional use only and issued with this special promo sleeve. It was distributed before the release of the album as a sample of the featured tracks and to promote the singles that were to be released. The tracks are listed on the back of the sleeve, 'The Kiss', 'Catch' b/w 'Just Like Heaven' and 'Why Can't I Be You?'. This pressing was unique to the UK.

KISS ME CD RADIO SAMPLER

ELEKTRA (2071–2)
This promotional sampler CD for 'Kiss Me,' was issued only in the USA. As well as six tracks from the LP, it includes a version of 'How Beautiful You Are' that at Fiction's request was specially remixed by Bob Clearmountain as a possible single. It is 45 seconds shorter than the LP version, but has remained unreleased as a single. Tracks were: 'Just Like Heaven', 'Catch', 'All I Want', 'The Perfect Girl', 'How Beautiful You Are (Remix)', 'Torture', 'Why Can't I Be You?'.

reverse

KISS ME FIRST AID BOX

The 'Kiss Me' First Aid box was a large 12'' promotional box set from the USA, put together by Elektra Records. It is often referred to by collectors, but rarely seen, as only approximately 100 were produced.

It contained a small Cure First Aid box with plasters etc., Chocolate Kisses, Red Hot Candy, Badges, A Biography, A Band Photo, A Letter From Elektra Records and Promo Copies of 'Kiss Me, Kiss Me, Kiss Me', 'Why Can't I Be You?' and 'Just Like Heaven' on vinyl, CD and cassette, although the contents seemed to vary slightly.

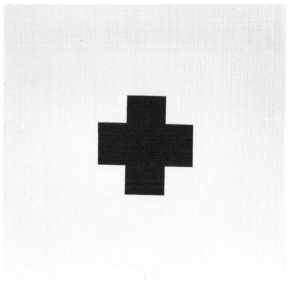

WHY CAN'T I BE YOU?
b/w A JAPANESE DREAM

UK 7'' (FICS 25)

UK Release – April, 1987

Some copies were issued with a sleeve sticker advertising the 12'' pressing.

UK 12'' (FICSX 25) features only two tracks, extended remixes of both songs. UK promo copies (FICSX 25 DJ) have the same two remixes.

Also issued in the UK was a limited edition 7'' double pack, in a gatefold sleeve, (FICSG 25), coupling the standard 7'' with live versions of 'Six different ways' and 'Push' on a bonus 7''. Both tracks were from 'The Cure In Orange'. Note the matrix number (FICSG 25) only appears on the bonus record. 10,000 copies were issued each individually numbered and have a different colour border to the standard sleeve.

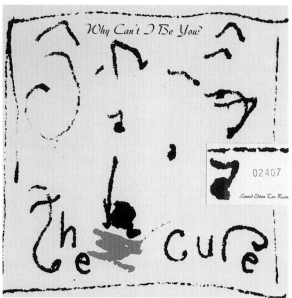

A CD single (888 454-2) was issued in Germany, and was available on UK import. This was the first CD single released by The Cure. It featured the same 2 tracks as the 12": 'Why Can't I Be You?' (extended) and 'A Japanese Dream' (extended).

A CDV (080 1842) was released in Europe in 1988 with the same two extended remixes as on the 12" (FICSX 25) and also included 'Hey You', a track from 'Kiss Me, Kiss Me, Kiss Me' that was missing on CD copies of the album.

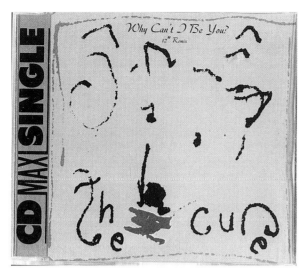

WHY CAN'T I BE YOU? b/w A JAPANESE DREAM
SOUTH AFRICAN POLYDOR (PD 2524)
This rare South African 7" pressing of 'Why Can't I Be You?' was also released but issued without a picture sleeve and distributed by Trutone.

WHY CAN'T I BE YOU?

PHILIPPINES 12"
POLYDOR (EP PRO 8428)
This very rare pressing from the Philippines was not issued with a picture sleeve, but note the mistake in the titles on the unusual sleeve sticker, which adds the word "with". Again, this has the same two tracks as the UK 12". In the Philippines Cure releases are manufactured and distributed by a company called Dyna under licence from Polydor. Due to the small singles market, 12" pressings are not always sold commercially, but are often used for promo purposes.

WHY CAN'T I BE YOU?

BRAZILIAN PROMO 12"
POLYDOR (2801 200)
Brazilian promo only pressings are renowned for having totally different and unique picture sleeves, although it must be noted that they are produced by Polydor Brazil and their design has no connection with Parched Art. This promo issue of 'Why Can't I Be You?' is often recognised as being the most unusual of all the Brazilian promotional 12" pressings.

It plays at 33 1/3 rpm and features the 7" b/w the 12" extended version of 'Why Can't I Be You?' referred to as 'Disco Mix' in Brazil. Note 'Promocional Invendavel' on the sleeve meaning 'Promo not for sale'. Needless to say this pressing is considerably rare and is perhaps the most distinctive of all 'Why Can't I Be You?' pressings.

WHY CAN'T I BE YOU?

ARGENTINIAN 12"
POLYDOR (23033)
Most Argentinian 12" singles are not sold commercially and are distributed only for promotional and radio use. Note the Spanish titles on this particular sleeve and on the label, also 'Difusion venta prohobida' meaning promo, not for sale. This features the same two tracks as the UK 12".

WHY CAN'T I BE YOU?
JAPANESE

'Why Can't I Be You' was the first release on the Japanese Polydor label and was the only single by The Cure released on three formats in Japan.

The 7" (5DM O183) was sold at a budget price. It has the same tracks as the UK 7". Note the small differences on this sleeve, most notably the blue mouth and grey border. The lyrics, a band picture and an advert for 'Kiss Me, Kiss Me, Kiss Me' are on the reverse of the sleeve.

This was the second and last single to be released as a 12" (13mm 7047) in Japan. It has the same remixed A and B sides as the UK 12". The lyrics to 'Why Can't I Be You?' are on the back of the obi and note how this Polydor obi incorporates the graphics and colour of the sleeve, unlike most of the previous releases on VAP.

The CDV (W18X 22008), as well as the video of 'Why Can't I Be You?' includes only two audio tracks, the 12" remixes of 'Why Can't I Be You?' and 'A Japanese Dream'. It does not include 'Hey You' as the European issue does.

81

CATCH

UK release – June, 1987
The single 'Catch' was not released in the USA or France. The A and B side tracks remain the same as the UK pressings on all releases of the single unless noted.

The UK 7'' (FICS 26) 'Catch' b/w 'Breathe' was pressed with both paper labels and injection mould labels. Some copies were also sold with a picture carrier bag of the 'Kiss Me, Kiss Me, Kiss Me' sleeve design, this was not a limited edition. Inscriptions in the run-off groove of this pressing read, side A 'What's that all about eh?' Side B 'Just for one change'. These were both phrases often used by Lol Tolhurst.

A limited edition of the 7'' (FICSP 26) was released with the same tracks, 'Catch' b/w 'Breathe', as a completely clear vinyl disc without any labels, and with a clear picture sleeve. This was a separate pressing to the standard 7'' and is without inscriptions in the run-off groove.

A very, very, small number of blank white 7'' picture discs (FICSP 26) of 'Catch' were made as test pressings for a possible release, but remained unreleased.

Worth noting is the Italian juke box promo single of 'Catch' (5000 751).

In 1988 'Catch' was released in Europe on CDV (080186–2) In addition to the video of 'Catch'. It featured 4 audio tracks 'Catch', 'Breathe' 'A Chain of Flowers' and the remix of 'Icing Sugar (New Mix)'.

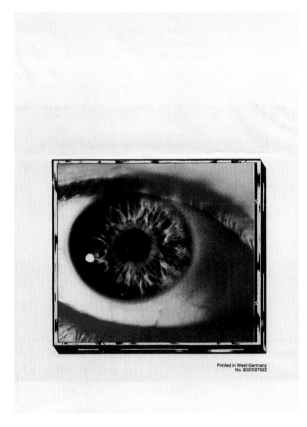

CATCH

CASSINGLE (FICSC 26)
The cassette of 'Catch' was the very first cassingle released by The Cure. It was issued only in the UK and plays the same 3 tracks each side. 'Catch', 'Breathe', and 'A Chain Of Flowers'. The design on the reverse of the cover is the same as the sleeve on the second 12'' (FICSE 26).

CATCH b/w BREATHE
JAPANESE 7''
(45 5DM 0197)

'Catch' was the last single released on vinyl in Japan and was also the last single from 'Kiss Me, Kiss Me, Kiss Me', as neither 'Just Like Heaven' nor 'Hot Hot Hot' were released there. This different sleeve is unique to the Japanese pressing and it features the same tracks as the UK 7''. It was not released as a 12'' in Japan, but was released on CDV (W18X 22011). The sleeve design to this was the same as the original UK sleeve.

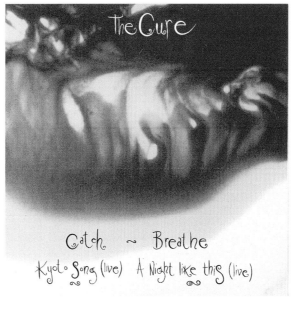

CATCH
UK 12''

Two 12'' pressings were released in the UK. The first (FICSX 26) 'Catch' b/w 'Breathe' and 'A Chain Of Flowers'. Some copies of this were issued with a title sticker on the sleeve. Shortly after, a second 12'' was released with a different sleeve design (an enlarged section of the original sleeve) and two live tracks from 'The Cure in Orange'. (FICSE 26) 'Catch' and 'Breathe' b/w 'Kyoto Song' (Live) 'A Night Like This' (Live).

Note the Spanish titles on the promo copy of the Argentinian 12'' Polydor (888 688-1). Also worth noting is the Brazilian Promo pressing Polydor (2801 209), issued with only a standard commercial sleeve but included the lyrics to 'Catch' on the reverse side.

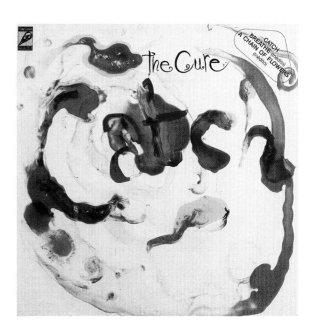

JUST LIKE HEAVEN

UK Release – October, 1987

'Just Like Heaven' was issued with a great variety of picture sleeves on numerous formats from within Europe and the US. Note the small Parched Art tea cup logo on the front of the sleeve. Whenever the handle is on the right side of the cup, it represents a design by Andy Vella. If the handle is on the left side, then the design is by Parched Art (Andy Vella with Porl Thompson). This single is slightly different from the version on 'Kiss Me, Kiss Me, Kiss Me'. The A and B side remain the same on all UK 7" pressings.

The standard UK 7" (FICS 27) 'Just Like Heaven' b/w 'Snow In Summer' was pressed with paper and injection mould labels. A very small, but unknown number of UK copies, with injection mould labels were mispressed,

playing 'Just Like Heaven' on both sides, despite the B side stating 'Snow In Summer'.

UK 12" (FICSX 27) 'Just Like Heaven' b/w 'Snow In Summer' and 'Sugar Girl' as an extra track. Promo 12" (FICSX 27 DJ) – same tracks.

Two limited editions were issued in the UK. Both pressings were limited to 10,000 copies and had the same standard A and B sides as before. The first was a white vinyl 7" (FICS 27) issued in a standard picture sleeve, each copy with an individually numbered sticker, although some copies were without this sticker. Plus a 7" picture disc (FICSP 27) was issued in a clear PVC picture sleeve. Both of these pressings state (FIC SW 27) in the run-off groove.

The Italian release is unique as the Italian dates of the Kissing tour are displayed on the sleeve of the 7'' (887104–7) and 12'' (887104–1).

Some Spanish copies featured a sleeve sticker listing the tour dates in Spain (887104-7).

Other pressings worth noting are a 7'' from the Philippines (POLYDOR PRO-3792) and a 7'' pressing from South Africa (PD 2563), neither was issued with a picture sleeve.

This UK CD (FIXCD 27) has the same tracks as the 12'' but the sleeve is a different painting of the design.

JUST LIKE HEAVEN
b/w BREATHE
FRENCH

'Catch' was not released in France so the French release of 'Just Like Heaven' was different from the UK.

Most copies of all the French pressings were issued with a sleeve sticker advertising that 'Just Like Heaven' was the theme tune of the French TV show Les Enfants Du Rock, a show that featured The Cure a number of times.

Two 7'' pressings of 'Just Like Heaven' were issued in France. The first, b/w 'Breathe' (887104–7), was issued with the black bordered sleeve. The 12'' (887104–1) pressing also featured a black border and sticker, b/w 'Breathe' and 'A Chain Of Flowers'.

Shortly after, a second 7'' (887104–7) pressing of 'Just Like Heaven' was issued. This time with the same sleeve and B side as the UK release and again with a sticker, b/w 'Snow In Summer'.

Mispressings of this release exist stating 'Snow In Summer', but playing the previous B side 'Breathe'. Also thought to exist is a mispressing of the first issue playing 'Snow In Summer' instead of the stated track 'Breathe'.

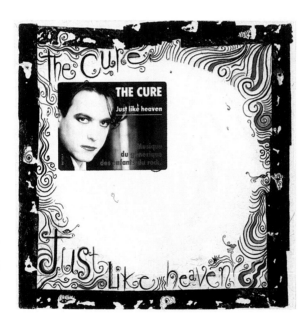

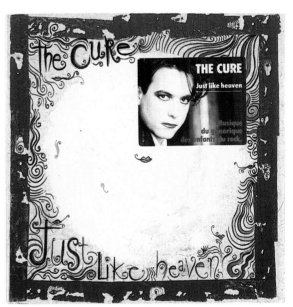

JUST LIKE HEAVEN
US/CANADA

As in France 'Catch' was not released in the USA or Canada so the tracks 'Breathe' and 'A Chain Of Flowers' were used as the B sides for 'Just Like Heaven' in both countries, instead of 'Snow in Summer' and 'Sugar Girl'. The blue border on the sleeve also changed to black for these releases and note, the letter 'R' in the word 'CURE' is different.

USA 7'' (769443) b/w 'Breathe' Canadian 7'' (9694437) b/w 'Breathe'.
   USA 12'' (066793) b/w 'Breathe' and 'A Chain Of Flowers'.
   Canadian 12'' (9667930) b/w 'Breathe' and 'A Chain Of Flowers'.

Typically, Elektra distributed large numbers of double sided 7'' and 12'' promo copies in the USA. The 12'' promo (ED 5252) was pressed with the LP version of 'Just Like Heaven' on the B side.
   Worth noting is the Argentinian 12'' pressing (Polygram 23052) which was also issued with a black bordered sleeve and has Spanish titles on the reverse.

reverse

Also released in the US was a cassingle with a card sleeve packaged in a long 12'' box (Elektra 966 7934). It featured the same three tracks on each side, 'Just Like Heaven', 'Breathe' and 'A Chain Of Flowers'.
   A CDV (Elektra 64002-2) was also released with the video of 'Just Like Heaven' and audio LP versions of only 'Catch', 'Hot, Hot, Hot' and 'Why Can't I Be You?'.

HOT HOT HOT !!!

UK Release – February, 1988
This was the first time four singles had ever been released from the same album. Both the A and B sides were remixes of tracks from 'Kiss Me, Kiss Me, Kiss Me'.

In the UK 'Hot, Hot, Hot' was released only on 12'' (FICSX 28) and CD single (FIXCD 28). Each format had the same tracks.
'Hot, Hot, Hot (Extended Remix)'
'Hot, Hot, Hot (Remix)'
'Hey You (Extended Remix)'.

Some copies of the CD included an insert advertising the release of the book *10 Imaginary Years*.

The UK 7'' of 'Hot, Hot, Hot' exists as a promotional pressing only, (FICSDJ 28) 'Hot, Hot, Hot (Remix)' b/w 'Hey You (Remix)'. This was distributed with its own titled promo sleeve and is the only UK single not released commercially as a 7''.

THE CURE

HOT HOT HOT !!!
(extended remix)

FICSXR 28
(887 329-1)

THE CURE

(extended remix)

A
45 rpm

FICSXR 28
(887 329-1)

REMIXED BY FRANCOIS KEVORKIAN

PROMO ONLY NOT FOR RESALE

FictioN

PROMO ONLY NOT FOR RESALE

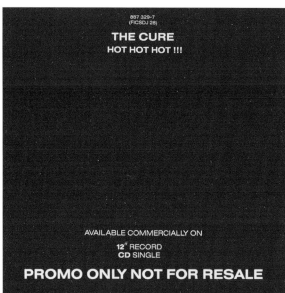

887 329-7
(FICSDJ 28)

THE CURE
HOT HOT HOT !!!

AVAILABLE COMMERCIALLY ON

12" RECORD
CD SINGLE

PROMO ONLY NOT FOR RESALE

HOT HOT HOT!!!
GERMAN 7" PROMO

Like the UK, a 7" was not released commercially in Germany and exists as a special promotional pressing only (887329–7), it features the same two tracks as the UK pressing and was also distributed with its own promo sleeve. This pressing has a small mistake on the A side label stating 'Francois Devorkian', instead of 'Francois Kevorkian', who remixed both versions of both tracks.

THE CURE

(extended remix)

(Smith – Gallup – Thompson – Williams – Tolhurst)

B
45 rpm

FICSXR 28
(887 329-1)

REMIXED BY FRANCOIS KEVORKIAN

PROMO ONLY NOT FOR RESALE

FictioN

HOT, HOT, HOT (EXTENDED) B/W HEY YOU (EXTENDED)
(FICSXR 28)

This promotional 12" pressing of only two tracks was also distributed in the UK and again with its own promo sleeve

1
THE CURE
Produced by Dave Allen & Robert Smith
PROMO ONLY NOT FOR RESALE

℗1988
Fiction Records

Made in
West Germany

FictioN

887 329-7

6444

STEREO 45

FictioN

Published by:
APB Music Co.
Ltd.

Hot Hot Hot (Remix) 3:33
(Smith/Gallup/Thompson/Williams/Tolhurst)
Remixed by Francois Devorkian &
Ron St. Germain

HOT HOT HOT!!!
USA/CANADA

In the US and Canada, a 7" was released commercially with a picture sleeve. US (7–69424), Canada (9694247) 'Hot, Hot, Hot (Remix)' b/w 'Hey You (Remix)'.

This promo 12" (ED 5273) that Elektra distributed widely had the LP and both single versions.

This cassingle packaged in a long 12" box was also available (9667834) and featured the same tracks as the UK CD single. Later in 1988 'Hot, Hot, Hot,'

b/w 'Why Can't I Be You?' (7–65967) was issued as part of Elektra's budget priced Spun Gold series of re-issued and re-packaged 7" singles. This was widely available in the US and in the UK on import. As a promotion by Sony for their 3" CD format 'Hot, Hot, Hot' was included on a CD in a promo package of 3 x 3" CDs which was issued in the US in 1988, and featured one compilation CD each from Elektra, WEA and Virgin Records.

THE CURE
HOT HOT HOT!!!
(extended remix) (7:05)
From the Elektra album, Kiss Me, Kiss Me, Kiss Me 60737

ELEKTRA

STEREO
33 1/3 RPM

the Cure
HOT HOT HOT!!!

ED 5273
A SIDE

PROMOTIONAL COPY
NOT FOR SALE

ELEKTRA

CASSETTE MAXI SINGLE CMS

THE CURE
HOT HOT HOT!!!

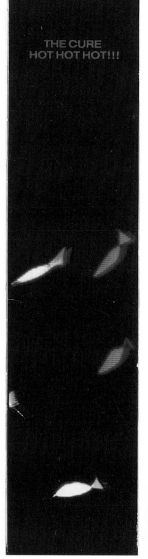

CASSETTE MAXI SINGLE CMS

THE CURE
HOT HOT HOT!!!

PEEL SESSIONS
KILLING AN ARAB,
10:15 SATURDAY NIGHT,
FIRE IN CAIRO,
BOYS DON'T CRY.

This particular record in the Strange Fruit series of Peel sessions is the only official release from the many sessions that The Cure recorded for *The John Peel Show* and also *The David Jenson Show*. In these shows songs like 'Forever', unusual versions of 'Primary' and 'Grinding Halt' and the unreleased 'Ariel' were performed.

This session of 'Killing An Arab', '10.15 Saturday Night', 'Fire In Cairo' and 'Boys Don't Cry', was the first Peel Session by The Cure, recorded on December 4, 1978. It was broadcast seven days later and released in 1988 on 12'' (SFP S050) and CD (SFP-SCD 050). A limited edition of the 12'' was issued with a metallic coloured sleeve. The CD was also on Japanese import and distributed by Jimc Records.

In 1991 this session was released by Strange Fruit on several limited editions of 7'' and 12'' coloured vinyl and 12'' picture disc. Foreign covers of the CD varied.

USA (DE18341-2) and Canadian (DE18341-2) issues were first released in a 12'' long package and a different sleeve. 'Killing An Arab' also features on a French compilation album 'Best Of Peel Sessions' and also on a bonus compilation CD given away with the early copies of the book 'In Session Tonight'.

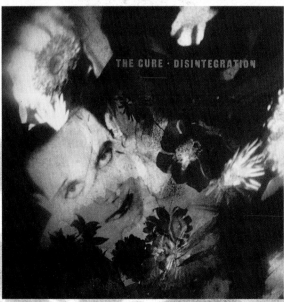

DISINTEGRATION

UK RELEASE – MAY, 1989
LP FIXH 14
Cassette FIXHC 14
CD 839353–2

Line up:
Robert Smith,
Simon Gallup,
Boris Williams,
Porl Thompson,
Roger O'Donnell,
Laurence Tolhurst

Side One
Plainsong
Pictures Of You
Closedown
Lovesong
Lullaby
Fascination Street

Side Two
Prayers For Rain
The Same Deep Water As You
Disintegration
Unititled

Extra tracks on CD and cassette
only: Last Dance & Homesick

Special limited edition signed copies of 'Disintegration' could be bought exclusively from branches of HMV on the 5th May, 1989, on the first come first served basis. This offer was advertised in *New Musical Express* of that week and each shop had approximately three to four copies. The sleeve is without the signature of Lol Tolhurst.

DISINTEGRATION
CD SAMPLER (DISIN 1)
This pre–release promotional album sampler for 'Disintegration' and the singles planned for release, was issued only on CD, indicating the phasing out of vinyl and the increasing use of CD for both promotional and commercial purposes.

Four tracks are featured from 'Disintegration': 'Lullaby', 'Pictures of You', 'Lovesong' and 'Plain Song'. All are album versions except the remixed single version of 'Lullaby'. This was issued only in the UK.

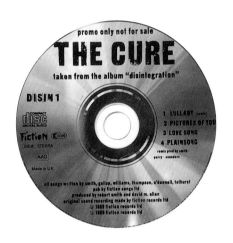

DISINTEGRATION
COLOMBIAN
POLYDOR (839353–1)
The Columbian pressing of 'Disintegration' was not released until 1990. The reverse of the sleeve was a completely different colour and the design was the wrong way up. Again, misprinted credits state Tulhurst.

HOMESICK
b/w **LAST DANCE**
CASSETTE (CURE C1)
This limited edition two track cassette features 'Homesick' on the A side and 'Last Dance' on the B side. It was given away with the first copies of 'Disintegration' which were sold on vinyl. This special offer was available only in Spain. 'Homesick' and 'Last Dance' were otherwise available only on the CD or cassette of 'Disintegration'.

reverse

THE CURE - DISINTEGRATION

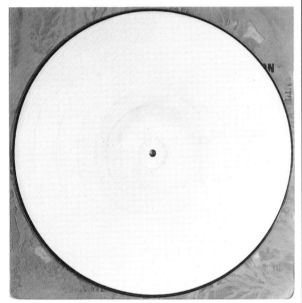

DISINTEGRATION
PICTURE DISC
(FIXHP 14)
UK release – May, 1990
Nearly one year after the original release of 'Disintegration', the LP was re–issued in the UK as a limited edition picture disc, in a special PVC picture sleeve. Test pressings for this record were pressed as plain white picture discs.

LULLABY
UK release – April, 1989
This single was a slightly different remixed version of 'Lullaby' from the version on 'Disintegration'. From 1989 onwards, it became standard practice for a CD single to be released as well as the 7'' and 12'' pressings. Surprisingly neither 'Lullaby' nor any other single from 'Disintegration' were ever released by Polydor in Japan.

The 7'' and 12'' A and B side tracks remain the same on all releases of 'Lullaby' unless noted.

UK 7'' (FICS 29) 'Lullaby' b/w 'Babble'. This issue was pressed with two different injection mould labels and a paper label. Promotional copies (FICSDJ 29) were distributed in the UK with different pink labels.

Two limited editions of the 7'' pressing were issued in the UK. Both were limited to 10,000 copies and individually numbered. The first edition (FICSG 29) had a gatefold sleeve with the lyrics to 'Lullaby' inside. It was sealed with a numbered sticker.

Later, a clear vinyl 7'' pressing was issued in a PVC picture sleeve (FICSP 29). Note, although these editions have new catalogue numbers, they were issued with standard (FICS 29) labels.

Worth noting is the 7'' Italian juke box single of 'Lullaby' b/w a different artist (AS 5000 820).

Released in the UK was a miniature 3'' CD with a gatefold sleeve (FICCD 29). It featured all four tracks, 7'' and extended version of 'Lullaby' with 'Babble' and 'Out Of Mind'.

Two 12''s were issued in the UK. (FICSX 29) 'Lullaby' (extended remix) b/w 'Babble' and 'Out Of Mind'. In addition to this, 10,000 copies were pressed on pink vinyl (FICVX 29) and issued as a limited edition with the same three tracks. Each copy was individually numbered.

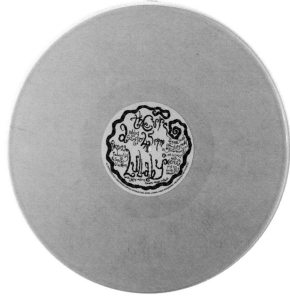

12'' Promo copies (FICSX DJ 29) were issued in the UK. These had distinctive pink labels as opposed to the usual plain titled labels of most other UK 12'' promos. Some copies were distributed with a sticker.

reverse

LULLABY
USA

Elektra did not release 'Lullaby' in the USA until several months later than the UK. As 'Babble' and 'Out Of Mind' had previously appeared as B sides on 'Fascination Street', live versions of 'Homesick' and 'Untitled' feature as the B side tracks. Both tracks were recorded during the Prayer tour and are also included on 'Entreat'. The reverse of the USA sleeve differs in colour from the UK.

7'' (7–69249) 'Lullaby' b/w 'Homesick' (Live)
Cassingle (9469249) 'Lullaby' 'Homesick' (Live)
12'' (066664) 'Lullaby' (extended) b/w 'Homesick' (Live) and 'Untitled' (Live)
CD (966664–2) 'Lullaby', 'Lullaby' (extended) 'Homesick' (Live) and 'Untitled' (Live)

FAIXA EXTRAÍDA DO LP
DISINTEGRATION

DISCO MIX PROMOCIONAL INVENDÁVEL

LULLABY
BRAZILIAN PROMO 12''
POLYGRAM (2801 340)

This rare promotional only pressing from Brazil was issued with a completely different sleeve and just two tracks: 'Lullaby' single version (although the titles state album version) b/w 'Lullaby' (extended).

LOVESONG

UK release – August, 1989
The sleeve design was by Maya and was one of the few sleeves not designed by Parched Art.
UK 7'' (FICS 30) 'Lovesong' b/w '2 late'.

White label promo copies (FICS 30) of this 7'' were also distributed.

As a limited edition of 10,000 copies the 7'' 'Love Box' (FICSG 30) was released which included a linen print of the artwork.

The Cassingle (FICCS 30) featured the same two tracks as the 7''.

Worth noting is the 7'' pressing of 'Lovesong' b/w 'Fascination Street' (7–65936) released as part of Elektra's Spun Gold series. 'Lovesong' also features with 'Just Like Heaven' on a two track
cassette issued as part of a similar series by Elektra. In Italy Polygram issued a typical promo juke box 7'' single of 'Lovesong' b/w a different artist (AS 5000 824).

The sleeve of the 12'' and CD was different in colour from the 7'' sleeve.

UK 12'' (FICSX 30) 'Lovesong' (extended) b/w '2 late' and 'Fear of Ghosts' as an extra track. These tracks remained the same on the UK promo copy (FICSX 30DJ) and all other 12'' commercial releases of 'Lovesong'. At one time rumours circulated among collectors and other sources that an unreleased 12'' picture disc of 'Lovesong' existed, of which only about 20 were pressed. However, this pressing does not exist and it was only ever a proposed limited edition. The idea was rejected.

In addition to these three tracks the CD (FICCD 30) included 'Lovesong' (7'' version) A CDV(081 398–2) was also issued in Germany and was on UK import.

Worth noting is the Brazilian 12'' promo (Polydor 2801373) with a different artist on the B side issued with just a red and yellow titled sleeve.

A very large number of 12'' promos (ED-5398) and many 12'' test pressings (ED-5390) of 'Lovesong' were distributed in the US.

Strictly Limited Edition, Individually Numbered
'LOVEBOX'
03130
INCLUDES ORIGINAL LINEN PRINT
Fiction   FICSG30

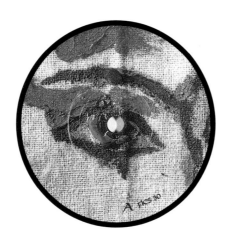

UK Promo 7''

LOVESONG VIDEO

This unique video compilation was distributed in the UK, for promotional use only, to larger record shops for in-store showing. It begins and ends with the video to 'Lovesong' and includes 'Boys Don't Cry', 'A Forest', 'Let's Go To Bed'. 'Close To Me' and 'Why Can't I Be You?'

It is particularly unusual among most other promo videos because of its special promotional cover which also has an illustrated album discography on the reverse.

STRANGER THAN FICTION (CIF CD3)
1989

This six track CD compilation was produced as a celebration of Fiction Records 10th year, and the bands, past and present, signed to the label.

Approximately 1,000 copies were distributed by Fiction, strictly for promotional use only.

It is of particular interest for the track 'To The Sky' by The Cure as this was the only recording made during the sessions for 'Kiss Me, Kiss Me, Kiss Me' that was never released. Also included was 'I Dig You' by Cult Hero, and Tim Pope's 'I Want To Be A Tree' (previously only ever pressed on vinyl).

Tracks featured are: 'I Dig You' Cult Hero 1979; 'Janice' – The Associates 1979; 'I Want To Be A Tree' – Tim Pope 1984; 'To The Sky' – The Cure 1987; 'Fatman' – Eat 1989; and 'Shake Down' – Die Warzau 1989.

STRANGER THAN FICTION, PART II
(PRCS 4293–4) 1991

Two years later, this rare five track cassette version of 'Stranger Than Fiction' was put together for a promotional only distribution in the USA. It featured The Cure's 'To The Sky' plus two tracks each from Die Warzau ('Funkopolis' and 'Burning') and Candyland ('Fountain O'Youth' and 'Bitter Moon') replacing the tracks by Cult Hero and Tim Pope etc.

PICTURES OF YOU

UK release – March, 1990
Mary Poole's photograph, taken by Robert Smith at the same time and place as the photograph on the 'Charlotte Sometimes' sleeve, also appears on the front of this sleeve. More editions of 'Pictures Of You' were released in the UK than of any other single. Shortly after this release Gallup/BPI limited the number of formats taken into consideration for UK chart purposes to four.

This version of 'Pictures Of You' was a shortened remix to the LP version. It was released in two groups and all of the B sides were recorded live at the 'Prayer Tour' and are also included on 'Entreat'.

Group A had a green colour sleeve design and featured:
7'' (FICA 34) 'Pictures Of You' b/w 'Last Dance'
Cassingle (FICCA 34) 'Pictures Of You' – 'Last Dance'
12'' (FICXA 34) 'Pictures Of You' (extended) b/w 'Last Dance,' 'Fascination Street'
CD (FICDA 34) 'Pictures Of You' – 'Last Dance' – 'Fascination Street'

In addition to these, a limited edition was released of the 7'' and the 12'' on green vinyl: 7'' (FICPA 34), 12'' (FIXPA 34). Each was individually numbered.

The sleeve and label of the first 12'' pressing (FICXA 34) had wrong credits stating that 'Pictures Of You' (extended) was remixed by Bryan Chuck New, but it was actually remixed by Saunders/Parry/Smith. On the green 12'' (FIXPA 34) the label credits were corrected and the sleeve was corrected by a sticker.

Group B was released in a purple coloured sleeve and with different B sides. The 12'' also featured a different remix of 'Pictures Of You'. They featured:
7'' (FICB 34) 'Pictures Of You' b/w 'Prayers For Rain'
Cassingle (FICCB 34) 'Pictures Of You' – 'Prayers For Rain'
12'' (FICXB 34) 'Pictures Of You' (strange mix) b/w 'Prayers For Rain' and 'Disintegration'
CD (FICDB 34) 'Pictures Of You', 'Prayers For Rain' – 'Disintegration'
The 7'' and 12'' were also released as a limited edition on purple vinyl: 7'' (FICPB 34), 12'' (FIXPB 34). Each was individually numbered.

PICTURES OF YOU

UK PROMO 12" (CURE–1)
This promotional 12" pressing
was distributed in the UK of
'Pictures Of You' (extended),
playing at 45 rpm and featuring
all four live tracks on the B side,
playing at 33 1/3 rpm: 'Last Dance',
'Prayers For Rain', 'Fascination
Street' and 'Disintegration'.

PICTURES OF YOU b/w
LOVESONG

(889 792 –7).
This unusual promotional
7" pressing was distributed in
Germany. It couples the A side,
'Pictures Of You' playing at 33 1/3
rpm with the previous single
'Lovesong' on the B side which
plays at 45 rpm. It was issued
with a plain title stickered sleeve
and is a unique German pressing.
An odd record which is rarely
ever found.

PICTURES OF YOU

POLYGRAM (AS 5000 837)
This Italian promo juke box single
was issued with a plain stickered
sleeve.

PICTURES OF YOU

USA
All the four B side tracks were
also available on the USA CD
release of 'Pictures Of You'
(966639–2).

This one track promo CD was
issued in the USA (PR 8165–2)
and was typical of the way Elektra
distributed promo CDs that present just the A side track. These
were issued in large numbers and
consequently are common.

FASCINATION STREET
1989
Elektra released a shortened remix of 'Fascination Street' instead of 'Lullaby' as the first single from 'Disintegration' in the USA and Canada. Both pressings had identical tracks featuring 'Babble' and 'Out Of Mind' as the B sides. Only in these two countries was this a single.

7" USA (7–69300), Canada (93007) b/w 'Babble'.
USA cassingle (4–69300) same two tracks.
Double A side 7" promo copies (7–69300) were distributed in the USA with standard picture sleeves.

An extended remix of 'Fascination Street' b/w 'Babble' and 'Out Of Mind' features on the 12" pressing.
USA (066 704), Canada (9667040).
Many 12" test pressings were issued and a large number of 12" promos were distributed in the US. The US CD (66702–2) featured all four tracks available on 7" and 12".
Worth noting is the 12" promo copy issued in Argentina (Polygram 602).
'Fascination Street' also appears in the film *Lost Angels* and was included on the film soundtrack album.

INTEGRATION
ELEKTRA (966633–2)
This box set is one of the few special editions of The Cure released in the US by Elektra Records. In the UK and other countries it was available on import. Although the sticker on the front presents it as a collector's edition of seventeen rare Cure tracks, it actually contains just the four standard US CD singles released from 'Disintegration': 'Fascination Street', 'Lovesong', 'Lullaby' and 'Pictures Of You'. 'Integration' also includes a small poster of The Cure.

ENTREAT
1990

Originally 'Entreat' was only available as a limited edition in France and the UK.

It was first available in France and offered by branches of FNAC as a bonus give away CD to anyone who bought three or more albums by The Cure at one time. It featured six live tracks recorded in July, 1989, during the Prayer tour at Wembley Arena: 'Pictures Of You', 'Closedown', 'Last Dance', 'Fascination Street', 'Prayers For Rain' and 'Disintegration'. Only the French issue (FIX F14) has a pink sleeve.

In the UK, 'Entreat' was offered as part of the promotion by Polydor Records called 'A Complete Cure'. This offered the twelve existing Cure albums at a discount price. A CD or cassette of 'Entreat' was then given away when two or more of the twelve albums were bought on any format from branches of HMV. In addition to the six tracks on the French issue, this included 'Homesick' and 'Untitled' as extra live tracks. The sleeve of both the CD (FIXCD 17) and cassette (FIXHC 17) were marked promotional use only – Not For Sale. Only this and the earlier French issue have card-type sleeves.

In March 1991 'Entreat' was released commercially in most countries as a budget priced LP (FIXH 17), CD (FIXCD 17) and cassette (FIXCS 17) with the same eight UK tracks, but again with a different coloured sleeve. Perhaps the most interesting was the Japanese release on CD (POCP–9018) which was issued in a shrink wrapped card package including a 30-page full colour booklet with an A-Z of The Cure's history.

THIRTEEN DOSES VIDEO

This unique promotional only video compilation was produced and distributed specifically for showing at branches of HMV only during the 'Entreat' and 'A Complete Cure' promotion. It is very rare and particularly distinctive for its special promo picture sleeve.

The Thirteen Doses are: '10.15 Saturday Night', 'Play For Today', 'Primary', The Hanging Garden', 'The Walk', 'The Lovecats', 'The Caterpillar', 'In Between Days', 'A Night Like This', 'Why Can't I Be You?', 'Just Like Heaven', 'Lullaby' and 'Pictures Of You'.

MIXED UP

UK RELEASE – NOVEMBER, 1990
LP FIXLP 18
Cassette FIXHC 18
CD FIXCD18

Line up:
Robert Smith,
Simon Gallup,
Porl Thompson,
Boris Williams,
Perry Bamonte

Side One
Lullaby (Extended Mix)
Close To Me (Closer Mix)
Fascination Street (Extended Mix)

Side Two
The Walk (Everything Mix)
Lovesong (Extended Mix)
A Forest (Tree Mix)

Side Three
Pictures Of You (Extended Dub Mix)
Hot Hot Hot!!! (Extended Mix)
Why Can't I Be You (Extended Mix)

Side Four
The Caterpillar (Flicker Mix)
In Between Days (Shiver Mix)
Never Enough (Big Mix)

MIXED UP
12" PROMOS

In addition to the CD sampler, three different 12" pressings were distributed in the UK to promote 'Mixed Up' and the singles to be released from the LP. They were issued in plain sleeves with the 'NON FICTION' logo, a newly formed part of Fiction Records in September, 1990.
'Close To Me' b/w 'The Walk' (Cure Promo1)
'Never Enough','Harold and Joe' b/w 'Let's Go To Bed' (Cure Promo2)
'A Forest' b/w 'In Between Days' (Cure Promo 3)

MIXED UP
PROMO CD SAMPLER
(CURE PRO CD1)
This UK promotional CD sampler featured four of the twelve remixed tracks from 'Mixed Up': 'The Walk' (Everything mix), 'Close To Me' (Closer mix), 'In Between Days' (Shiver mix) and 'Never Enough' (Big mix).
   A four track CD sampler for 'Mixed Up' was also issued in France. All the songs from 'Mixed Up' were previewed by The Cure's pirate radio station Cure FM which was broadcast from Fiction Records, and shortly afterwards by Cure 102 FM.

105

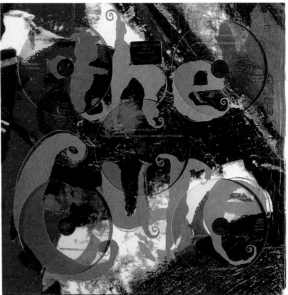

MIXED UP 5CD BOX
POLYDOR (867529–2)
In 1991 a limited edition of 2,500 shrink wrapped 12'' picture boxes of 'Mixed Up' was released in France, featuring all twelve 'Mixed Up' tracks on five picture CDs. All standard issues of the CD had only eleven tracks, missing 'Why Can't I Be You?' (Extended mix). The extended version of 'Lullaby' in this edition is 50 seconds shorter than on the normal CD release.

ASSEMBLAGE
POLYDOR (511 124–2)
In 1991, the first twelve albums on CD were packaged together as the 'Assemblage' box set. Each CD had a card sleeve and a booklet was included. The front of the box opened with revolving graphics underneath. Again, this was only released in France, but was available on import in the UK. It was limited to 2,500 copies.

THE CURE
AN INTERVIEW
(CURE PRO CD3)
Two interviews are featured on this disc. The first is a 36 minute interview with Janice Long in which Robert Smith talks in detail about the 'Mixed Up' album, Cure FM, previous singles and The Cure itself. The second is the same interview repeated without Janice Long's voice in order that other voices can be dubbed in for radio use.

This was only issued on CD and was produced for promotional use in the UK only.

NEVER ENOUGH

UK Release – September, 1990
'Never Enough' was the only new song on the 'Mixed Up' album. This single varied slightly among foreign releases with perhaps the Japanese issue being the most distinctive.

As standard, the UK 7'' was pressed with two labels, paper and injection mould.
UK 7'' (FICS 35) 'Never Enough' b/w 'Harold and Joe'.

In the UK white label 7'' test pressings (FICS 35) were distributed to DJ's for promo use but in considerably small numbers as the more common promo 12'' (Cure Promo2) was already in circulation. The label of this 7'', unlike other UK promos has handwritten titles (on the A side only) and was issued with a plain sleeve with a round title sticker. The Cassingle (FICCS 35) has the same tracks.

The UK 12'' (FICSX 35) featured 'Never Enough' (Big mix) 'Harold And Joe' b/w 'Let's Go To Bed' (Milk mix)
Many of the commercial copies state (CURE PROMO 2) in the run-off groove. These copies were originally pressed for promo use.

In addition to commercial copies 12'' promos were issued by Elektra in the USA with the same three tracks as the UK but played at 33 1/3 rpm (ED–5489).

Worth noting is the 12'' Brazilian promo of 'Never Enough (Big Mix)' with 'Close To Me (Closer Mix)' on the same side b/w a different artist and with just a plain titled sleeve, Polygram (2801468).

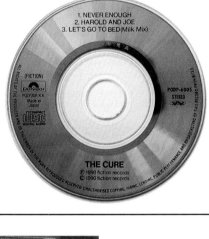

1. NEVER ENOUGH
2. HAROLD AND JOE
3. LET'S GO TO BED(Milk Mix)

PODP-6005
STEREO

THE CURE
℗ 1990 fiction records
© 1990 fiction records

NEVER ENOUGH
UK CD
In addition to the standard UK CD (FICCD 35), a limited edition of 10,000 copies was issued as a picture CD (FICDP 35) with a window sticker on the front. Each CD had the same tracks 'Never Enough (Big Mix)', 'Harold and Joe' and 'Let's Go To Bed (Milk Mix)'. This was the only limited edition of the single.

NEVER ENOUGH
JAPANESE 3'' CD
(PODP–6005)
In Japan only 'Never Enough' was released as a 3'' CD and was not available on any other format. This was the only single from 'Mixed Up' released in Japan . This example is one of the scarce promotional copies that were distributed, stating 'Sample Disc - Not for Sale' in the red square on the sleeve and on the disc itself. Both commercial and promotional copies have the same tracks, 'Never Enough', 'Harold And Joe' and 'Let's Go To Bed (Milk Mix)'.

CLOSE TO ME (REMIX)
UK Release – October, 1990
This new remixed version of the original single was available as two versions, 'Close To Me (Closest Mix)' and 'Close To Me (Closer Mix)'. All but one of the B sides and extra tracks were new remixes of previous singles. The A and B sides remained the same on all 7'' releases. This single was not released in Japan.

UK 7'' (FICS 36)
Close To Me (Closest Mix) b/w Just Like Heaven (Dizzy Mix) Note the different label of the UK Promo copy (FICSDJ 36). These were distributed in standard sleeves.
UK cassingle (FICCS 36)
Same two tracks.

The UK 12" pressing (FICSX 36) featured Close To Me (Closer Mix) b/w Just Like Heaven (Dizzy Mix) and Primary (Red Mix)

Promotional and commercial 7" pressings (879146–7) from Spain have misprinted label titles stating 'Closet Mix' and not 'Closest Mix'.

Many 12" promotional copies (FD 5513) were issued in the USA with the same three tracks and a titled sleeve sticker. Like most 12" pressings from the USA, it played at 33 1/3 rpm.

CLOSE TO ME
UK CD

Two CDs were issued in the UK. In addition to the two 7" tracks, the first CD (FICCD 36) featured 'Primary (Red Mix)'.

Later a second CD was released, with a slightly different sleeve (FICDR 36) and was the only limited edition of the single. 10,000 copies were issued, each individually numbered and shrink wrapped in a 10" package with a poster. It featured 'Close To Me (Closer Mix)', 'Just Like Heaven (Dizzy Mix)' and 'Why Can't I Be You? (Extended)'.

American copies of the CD (Elektra 66582–2) were issued with Digi packs and a different design on the CD.

One track promo picture CDs (PRCD 8276–2) were also distributed in the US.

A FOREST (REMIX)
FRENCH 1990

This third single from 'Mixed Up' was released only in France. The B side was also from the album and the 12'' included the original 5.50 LP version of 'A Forest'.

7'' (867384–7)
'A Forest' (Tree mix) b/w
'In Between Days' (shiver mix)
Cassingle (867384–4) same tracks
12'' (867385–1)
'A Forest' (Tree mix) b/w
'In Between Days' and 'A Forest'
CD (867385–2) same tracks

This Promotion 12'' pressing (2137) of this single was also distributed in France. These had their own promo picture sleeve and featured just two tracks, 'A Forest (Tree Mix)' b/w 'In Between Days (Shiver Mix)'.
   Note 'Hors commerce' on the label meaning 'Not For Sale'. These two tracks also featured on a promo CD (4087) also distributed in France for this single.

A FOREST PROMO CD
(4112)
Around the same time as the French release of 'A Forest' this two track CD single of 'A Forest' (Tree Mix) and 'In Between Days' (Shiver Mix) was given away free, shrink wrapped with any Cure album bought on CD for a limited period. This offer was only available in France. The design on this bonus CD, of which some copies had gold titles and others silver, is different from the standard edition of the single.

PICTURE SHOW
POLYGRAM (083096-3)
UK Release – June, 1991
'Picture Show' was a follow up video compilation to 'Staring At The Sea' featuring the videos for the ten singles that were released after 'Close To Me' from 1986 onwards. Included were the 12" extended versions of the videos for 'Why Can't I Be You?' and 'Hot Hot Hot' with home movie footage between each film.

THE CURE PLAY OUT
WINDSONG (WIV 007)
UK Release – December, 1991
'Play Out' was recorded over January and February 1991 and takes place over seven days. In these seven days the Cure play five live performances including the T&C2 London and MTV's 'Unplugged', together with various pieces of additional home movie and back stage film. It was produced by The Cure and Chris Parry. Time coded promotional copies include two additonal tracks recorded at the T&C2, 'Killing An Arab' and '10.15 Saturday Night'.

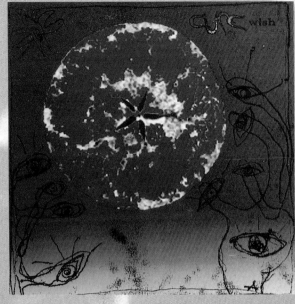

WISH

UK RELEASE – APRIL, 1992
LP FIXH 20
Cassette FIXHC 20
CD FIXCD 20

Line up:
Robert Smith,
Simon Gallup,
Porl Thompson,
Boris Williams,
Perry Bamonte

Side One
Open
High
Apart

Side Two
From The Edge Of The Deep
Green Sea
Wendy Time
Doing The Unstuck

Side Three
Friday I'm In Love
Trust
A Letter To Elise

Side Four
Cut
To Wish Impossible Things
End

WISH PROMO BOX SET

This 9" box set was specially produced for promotional use only. It was distributed in small numbers in the UK, some were also sent to France for distribution. It contains a CD of 'Wish' in a promotional only digipack packaging with artwork that differs from the commercial release. Each of these was personalised with the printed name of the person to whom they were issued. Also included was a standard cassette of 'Wish' and the 'Wish' electronic press kit (CURE PK1), a promotional video that featured an animated introduction, an interview with The Cure at the Manor Studios and a brief look at the making of the videos for 'High' and 'Friday I'm In Love'.

WISH INTERVIEW DISC

(CID 1)

This interview disc was issued only on CD and for promotional distribution only. It features an interview recorded at the Manor Studios in Oxford with Robert Smith, Simon Gallup and Perry Bamonte talking about the album.

Carrier given away with copies of Wish

113

LIBERATION CD

(4223)

This unique promotional CD was given away in an exclusive competition by the French newspaper *Liberation*. Anyone answering the three set questions correctly won the CD. It featured three tracks from 'Wish', 'Wendy Time', 'A Letter To Elise' and 'Cut' and was issued with its own numbered Digi pack gatefold sleeve.

FIVE LIVE CD

(CURE 1)

'Five Live' was a limited edition, available only in Australia. It was given away as a bonus CD with copies of 'Wish'. It is a unique compilation of five live tracks, three from the album 'Concert' and two from the album 'Entreat'. Tracks are 'Primary', 'A Forest', 'Pictures Of You', 'Fascination Street' and '10.15 Saturday Night'. A small misprint on the back of the sleeve credits '10.15 Saturday Night' to Thompson and not Tolhurst.

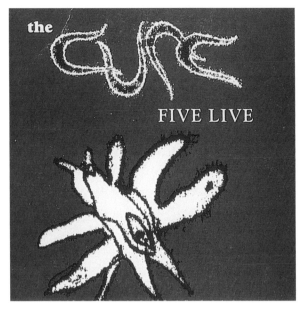

WISH
CD LIMITED EDITION

The CD of 'Wish' was also issued as a limited edition with special card packaging by Virgin Record stores in Australia. Each package was individually numbered and included a picture card of the band.

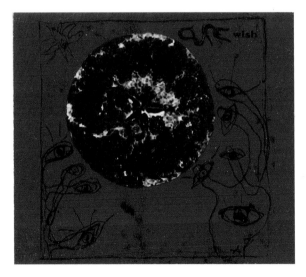

PURE CURE

ELEKTRA (CURE 1)

The 'Pure Cure Compilation' CD was produced and issued by Elektra Records in Canada strictly for promotional use only. It features a unique compilation of fourteen tracks by The Cure including 'Hello, I Love You'. Like most promotional CDs from Elektra, this was issued without a front picture sleeve and with only titles on the reverse but is considerably rare. Tracks were: 'Open', 'High (Higher Mix)', 'A Letter To Elise', 'From The Edge of The Deep Green Sea', 'Just Like Heaven', 'Why Can't I Be You?', 'Never Enough (Big Mix)', 'Fascination Street', 'In Between Days', 'The Lovecats', 'Boys Don't Cry', 'Love Song', 'Close To Me (Closer Mix)' and 'Hello I Love You'.

The Cure's version of 'Hello I Love You' (originally by The Doors) was recorded for inclusion as the first song on 'Rubaiyat', an American forty track compilation of Elektra artists performing songs by other artists on the label. It was released to celebrate Elektra's 40th anniversary. A six second reprise of 'Hello I Love You' by The Cure features as the last track on the album. Also included is a cover version of 'In Between Days' by John Eddie. 'Rubaiyat' was also released in the UK and Europe.

UK CD BOX SET

This UK box set featured a complete package of the 15 albums on CD from 'Three Imaginary Boys' to 'Wish'. It was issued as a limited edition and was also available without the CD's.

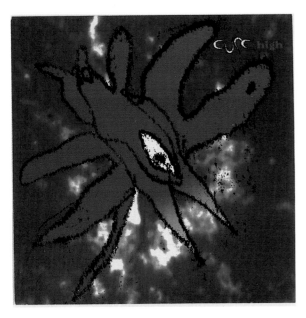

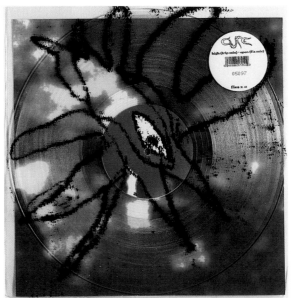

HIGH

UK Release – March, 1992
Because of the restrictions on the number of formats considered by BPI/Gallup in the UK, 'High' was released with two separate catalogue numbers. The first four issues were FIC 39, the additional two were issued as FIC 41. No vinyl of 'High' was released in the USA.

The A and B sides remain the same as the UK on all 7'' pressings.
UK 7'' (FICS 39) 'High' b/w 'This Twilight Garden'
UK cassingle (FICCS 39) same two tracks.
Two 12'' pressings were released in the UK.
(FICSX 39) 'High' (Higher mix) b/w 'This Twilight Garden' and 'Play'
UK Promo copies (FICSX 39DJ) featured the same tracks.
The second 12'' (FICSX 41) featuring 'High' (Trip mix) b/w 'Open' (Fix mix) was issued as a limited edition clear vinyl pressing, with new tracks. Each was individually numbered.

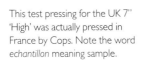

The UK CD included a lyric picture card and was issued in a special picture box with space for later CD singles. (FICCD 39) 'High', 'This Twilight Garden', 'Play', 'High' (Higher mix). Cure balloons were given away when a copy of 'High' was bought, but were not part of any limited edition package. Later, the CD was issued without the box and with catalogue number (FICCD 41).

This test pressing for the UK 7'' 'High' was actually pressed in France by Cops. Note the word *echantillon* meaning sample.

HIGH
b/w HIGH
BRAZILIAN PROMO 12"
POLYGRAM (280 1569)
Despite the standard sleeve of the
Brazilian CD single, this Brazilian
promo 12", a double sided pressing of 'High' (7" version), was still
issued with a unique, completely
different sleeve.

HIGH
FRENCH PROMO CD
(4211)
Polydor issued two promo CDs
in France for 'High'. Both have all
four tracks and the same catalogue
number (4211) but have different
sleeves. One has a unique promo
card sleeve and lists the titles on
the reverse. The other had a
standard commercial sleeve design
but opened up to list magazines
in which The Cure appeared.

HIGH
BRAZILIAN CD
(M–865565–2)
As one of the very first commer-
cial singles released in Brazil,
'High' was issued as a four track
CD single (M–865565–2). Note
the background on the sleeve
design of this, and the USA issue,
differs from the UK.

FRIDAY I'M IN LOVE

UK Release – May, 1992
UK 7'' (FICS 42) 'Friday I'm In Love' b/w 'Halo'
Cassingle (FICCS 42) featured same tracks.

UK CD (FICCD 42) 'Friday I'm In Love', 'Halo', 'Scared As You', 'Friday I'm In Love (Strangelove Mix)' Worth noting is the Japanese CD (POCP–1223) with the same four tracks, including a Japanese biography and lyrics.

Also worth noting is the two track CD single and the four track CD single which were released in the US and France. No vinyl was released in the US.

Worth noting is this Japanese CD single (POCP – 1189) with the same tracks, but with a different coloured disc.

USA CD
As no vinyl of 'High' was released in the US, two CD singles were released instead, both with designs on the disc that were slightly different from the UK edition. One was a CD with all four tracks in a digipack, the other was a two track CD (64766–2) in a card sleeve that featured 'High' and 'Open (Fix Mix)'. This was one of very few releases that featured the Fix Mix of 'Open'.

Test pressing produced in France for the UK 7''

FRIDAY I'M IN LOVE
UK 12''
The UK 12'' pressing of 'Friday I'm In Love' (FICSX 42) was released on multicoloured vinyl only and was widely available in various colours. Promotional copies (FICSX 42DJ) were the only UK pressing of the 12'' on black vinyl, and both have the same tracks. 'Friday I'm In Love (Strangelove Mix)' b/w 'Halo' and 'Scared As You' as an extra track. European (Polydor 863067-1) and all other pressings were on standard black vinyl.

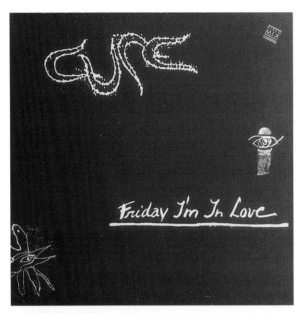

FRIDAY I'M IN LOVE

BRAZILIAN 12" PROMO
POLYGRAM (2801 583)
This rare 12" promo pressing
was distributed in Brazil. It was a
double sided pressing of the 7"
version of 'Friday I'm In Love',
playing at 33 1/3 rpm. It is odd
amongst other Brazilian promos
as the sleeve, although unique,
includes standard album artwork
in its design.

FRIDAY I'M IN LOVE

FRENCH PROMO CD
FICTION (5423)
This two track promotion CD of
'Friday I'm In Love' and 'Halo' was
distributed only in France with its
own special promo sleeve.

THE BIG HAND (LIVE)
A LETTER TO ELISE (LIVE)

12" ACETATE – 1991
Because of the nature of an
acetate, it is often cut with an
unreleased version or mix of a
song that will never reach the
public ear. This particular 12"
acetate features very distinctive
live versions of two songs from
two very low key live performances. On one side is 'The Big
Hand' recorded at the T&C 2
Club, London, on January 17,
1991, and on the reverse is 'A
Letter To Elise' recorded for
MTV's *Unplugged*, on January 24,
1991. Only three or four of these
would have been cut, most likely
during the production of 'The
Cure Play Out' video.

A LETTER TO ELISE

UK release – October, 1992
Before the release of 'A Letter To Elise' and 'The Big Hand', both songs were previewed for the first time live when The Cure played a secret date on January 17, 1991, at the T&C 2, London, under the name of '5 Imaginary Boys'.

No limited editions of this single were released, nor was it released on 7'' or 12'' in the USA, Japan or Australia and New Zealand.
UK 7'' (FICS 46) 'A Letter To Elise' b/w 'The Big Hand'
This issue was pressed with both paper labels and injection mould labels.
UK Cassingle (FICCS 46) – same two tracks
UK CD (FICCD 46) 'A Letter To Elise', 'The Big Hand', 'A Foolish Arrangement' 'A Letter To Elise' (blue mix) issued with a lyric picture card.
UK 12'' (FICSX 46) 'A Letter To Elise' (blue mix) b/w 'The Big Hand' and 'A Foolish Arrangement' as an extra track.
All UK 12'' copies were issued with a special clear PVC picture sleeve and insert. All other European 12'' pressings were issued with standard picture sleeves. UK promo copies (FICSX 46DJ) featured the same tracks and were issued with a plain sleeve.
Worth noting is the Brazilian 12'' promo pressing of 'A Letter To Elise' (Fontana 2801625), playing at 33 1/3 rpm It is b/w a completely different artist, playing at 45 rpm and was not issued with a picture sleeve.

A LETTER TO ELISE

JAPANESE CD
(POCP–1258)
'A Letter To Elise' was released only on CD in Japan and was the first time three singles from one LP had been released there.

SHOW

UK RELEASE – SEPTEMBER, 1993
LP FIXH 25
Cassette FIXHC 25
CD FIXCD 25

Line up:
Robert Smith,
Simon Gallup,
Porl Thompson,
Boris Williams,
Perry Bamonte

Side One
Tape
Open
High
Pictures Of You
Lullaby

Side Two
Just Like Heaven
Fascination Street
A Night Like This
Trust
Doing The Unstuck

Side Three
The Walk
Let's Go To Bed
Friday I'm In Love
In Between Days
From The Edge Of The Deep Green Sea

Side Four
Never Enough
Cut
End

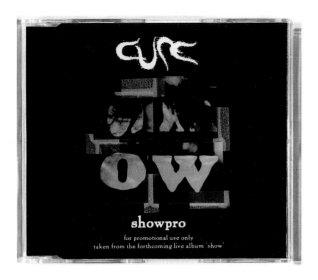

SHOW PRO
(SHOWPRO 1)
'Show Pro' was issued for promotional distribution only, before
the release of 'Show'. It features
just two tracks from the album
'Just Like Heaven' and 'Doing The
Unstuck' and was only issued as
a CD. 'Doing The Unstuck' was
once planned as a single from
'Show' but was never actually
released. Consequently no singles
were taken from the album.

A Spanish copy of 'Show Pro'
with the same two tracks was
issued, although without a picture
sleeve.

In the US Elektra widely
distributed a one track only
promo CD of 'Just Like Heaven'
(PRCD 8825–2) as a promotion
for' Show'.

SHOW
VIDEO
POLYGRAM (087742-3)
UK release – September, 1993
'Show' was filmed live during the
Wish tour 1992 at The Palace,
Michigan, USA. Released simulta-
neously with the album 'Show'
it included five extra tracks not
on the album or the 18 track
version of 'Show' that was shown
at cinemas, 'To Wish Impossible
Things', 'Primary', 'Boys Don't
Cry', 'Why Can't I Be You?' and
'A Forest'. This live film of 'Show'
was also released on laser disc
(POLYGRAM 087742-1).

SIDE SHOW

'Side Show' was a CD single released only in Australia and the US by Elektra Records. It featured five live tracks from 'Show'– 'Tape', 'Just Like Heaven', 'Fascination Street', 'The Walk' and 'Let's Go To Bed'. Four of these were unavailable on the Australian and American CD release of 'Show' as they were issued with only fourteen tracks and as a single CD album. Australian copies (4509–93658–2) have card sleeves while the American copies (66275–2) are issued with a Digi pack.

SHOW

JAPANESE CD
(POCP – 1363/4)
The Japanese CD is worth noting as it features a different sleeve with slightly different coloured discs to all other releases of 'Show'. A sticker of the UK sleeve design is included also.

PARIS PRO

(PARIS PRO 1)

'Paris Pro' was distributed in the UK for promotional use only as a preview to the album 'Paris'. Like the similar styled 'Show Pro' it existed as a CD only and featured only two tracks from the album, 'Catch' and 'Play For Today'.

PARIS

UK RELEASE – OCTOBER, 1993
LP FIXH 26
Cassette FIXHC 26
CD FIXCD 26

Line up:
Robert Smith,
Simon Gallup,
Porl Thompson,
Boris Williams,
Perry Bamonte

<u>Side One</u>
The Figurehead
One Hundred Years

<u>Side Two</u>
At Night
Play For Today
Apart

<u>Side Three</u>
In Your House
Lovesong
Catch
A Letter To Elise

<u>Side Four</u>
Dressing Up
Charlotte Sometimes
Close To Me

FRIDAY I'M IN LOVE (LIVE) LOVESONG (LIVE)

ELEKTRA (PRCD 8891–2)

Issued for promotional use only in the USA by Elektra, this CD features a live version of 'Friday I'm In Love' taken from the album 'Show' and of 'Lovesong' from 'Paris'.

EAT XPECTATIONS

LP (XFMLP 1)
CD (XFMCD 1)
CASSETTE (XFMMC 1)

This compilation album was recorded live at the XFM Great Xpectations concert arranged in support of the radio station XFM. It includes two tracks from The Cure's headlining performance, 'Just Like Heaven' and 'Disintegration'.

PURPLE HAZE

The version of 'Purple Haze' that The Cure recorded with Brian 'Chuck' New for the Jimi Hendrix tribute album 'Stone Free' was specially chosen as the second song to be aired on the first official transmission day of Virgin 12.15 a.m. Radio. No promotional copies of this version were pressed at all. The version that featured on the 'Stone Free' album was different to this, being remixed by Robert Smith and Brian 'Chuck' New.

This double sided promotional 12''(PRO–A–6704) of the 'Stone Free' 5.21 album version was pressed and issued by Reprise Records with a plain sleeve. Also issued in the USA was a two track promo CD (PRO–CD–6704–R). This featured the LP version and a 3.59 edit version.

THE CROW

ATLANTIC (7567–82519–2)
UK release – March, 1994
Originally the makers of 'The Crow' approached Robert Smith wanting to use 'The Hanging Garden' in their film, as the lyrics to the song are quoted in the comic after which the film is titled. Instead, Robert Smith preferred to record something new, but in keeping with the sound of 'The Hanging Garden'. The Cure then recorded the track 'Burn' specially for the film soundtrack. 'Burn' is not included on, nor has it been pressed as, any promotional 7'', 12'' or CD. It features only on the CD and cassette of 'The Music From The Film The Crow'. Atlantic released the album slightly earlier in the US but did not release on vinyl at all.

GLOSSARY OF TERMS

ACETATE

An acetate is the very first disc that is produced from a recording. It acts as a one–off listening device for the producer or the band to hear a recording or mix of a track.

The name acetate refers to the material from which the disc is made. It will be produced on a cutting machine which will cut the grooves into the acetate. These discs have a metal base plate through their middle, and only three or four will be cut. The sound quality of acetates deteriorates quickly and they do not last for many plays.

PROMOTIONAL OR PROMO COPY

A promo copy of a record will be distributed to radio stations, record shops, DJs, journalists on the music press, and within the record company itself, as a preview before the commercial release of a single or album.

A promo copy will normally have the same tracks as the commercial issue, but will probably be distinguished by a "promo copy only, not for sale" stamp on the label or maybe a completely different label from the commercial release, and possibly a slightly different catalogue number. The number of promo copies issued is very much less than the commercial release, varying from a few hundred to as many as a few thousand.

PROMOTIONAL ONLY PRESSING

To appreciate the nature of these records, an important distinction must be made between promo copies of a release and promotional only pressings. A promotional only pressing is pressed purely for promotional use and will not be released commercially. It will often feature a unique coupling or collection of tracks on a particular format. Generally, promotional only records are much rarer than promo copies.

SAMPLER

This is usually a 12" or CD. A sampler will be specially produced and distributed for promotional use only and will feature a unique compilation of maybe three or four selected tracks from a forthcoming album. Often will have a special cover that differs from anything released commercially.

TEST PRESSING

A test pressing is the very first pressing of a single or album and is pressed before any promotional or commercial copies. It is made to check the quality of the pressing. Generally, between five and 10 test pressings will be made. These will often have pressing plant labels stating the date they were pressed or maybe a plain hand written label.

CATALOGUE NUMBER

Refers to the reference number given to each issue or release of a single or album. Catalogue numbers are used primarily by warehouses and record shops to maintain stock levels and to re-order a particular record.

MATRIX NUMBER

Refers to the catalogue number in the run off groove which will have additional digits distinguishing the A and B sides.

TEST PRESSING PROMO

This refers to records that are pressed directly after the test pressings for promo use but are not issued with special promo labels. Instead they are issued with plain labels or they have only a number one and a number two which give no details of the content of the record. These are mainly found in the UK and are often issued in a plain sleeve with a title sticker. Despite the term, these cannot be considered as true test pressings.

ITALIAN PROMO JUKE BOX SINGLES

In addition to standard Italian pressings, these promo 7"s are specially produced in Italy for juke box and promo use. These singles present a different artist on each side and are only ever issued with plain white sleeves with title stickers, although they are sometimes found with unusual and poor quality picture sleeves that are definitely not official.

DOUBLE SIDED PROMO

A 7" or 12" pressing that has the same track on both sides of the record. Many promos from the USA fall into this category, often presenting the A-side track only. Unlike most other countries, the US chiefly produces promos in very large numbers and they are very common.

Thanks to Michael Dempsey, Ken Prust, Nigel Vichi, Mady, Janie, Chris, Johannes, Brian, Lanya, Pascal M, Chriss, Leeann and Rita.
Any comments or additional information on the items within this book or on any other unmentioned official pressings, picture sleeves etc. would be very welcome and gratefully received.
Contact: Daren Butler, c/o Chris Charlesworth, Omnibus Press, 8/9 Frith Street, London W1V 5TZ.